Black-naped oriole on a Eugenia (*Oriolus chinensis*)
Wellesley Collection

NATURAL HISTORY DRAWINGS
IN THE INDIA OFFICE
LIBRARY

By Mildred Archer

LONDON

Published for the Commonwealth Relations Office by
HER MAJESTY'S STATIONERY OFFICE

1962

First published 1962
Second impression 1964

© *Crown copyright* 1962

Published by
HER MAJESTY'S STATIONERY OFFICE

To be purchased from
York House, Kingsway, London W.C.2
423 Oxford Street, London W.I
13A Castle Street, Edinburgh 2
109 St. Mary Street, Cardiff
39 King Street, Manchester 2
50 Fairfax Street, Bristol I
35 Smallbrook, Ringway, Birmingham 5
80 Chichester Street, Belfast I
or through any bookseller

Price £1 7s. 6d. net

The Arms depicted on the title page and cover are those of the Honourable East India Company. They were granted to the 'New' East India Company in 1698 and were adopted by the 'United' Company in 1709

PREFACE

THE Natural History drawings described in this Catalogue consist of some 5000 drawings of plants and animals from India and South-East Asia, executed mainly by Indian artists in British employment, but including a small number by British and Chinese artists. Though almost all the drawings were made in order to serve as a record of botanical and zoological species, the information which they convey has for the most part long since been incorporated in the textbooks of fauna and flora. Such value as they have today is accordingly artistic and historical rather than scientific. They were the product of a re-markable enthusiasm for the study of natural history which developed among the British in India and the East Indies at the end of the eighteenth century and in the early years of the nineteenth century, an enthusiasm shared alike by the amateur and the professional student, by the private traveller and the East India Company official. In the historical introduction to her Catalogue, describing the circumstances in which the drawings came to be executed, to be formed into collections, and to find their way eventually into the India Office Library, Mrs Archer has thus thrown light upon a curious and hitherto little explored aspect of the life and activity of the British in India in Company days.

The arrangement and description of the other art collections in the Library (the Persian miniatures, the Indian miniatures, and the European paintings and drawings) was put in hand some years ago, and it is hoped that catalogues of them will follow the present volume without undue delay.

May 1961

S. C. SUTTON
Librarian

ACKNOWLEDGEMENTS

During the preparation of this catalogue I have been greatly assisted by the late Sir Norman Kinnear, former Director of the British Museum (Natural History), Mr J. R. Sealy, Principal Scientific Officer, Kew Herbarium, and Mr W. G. Archer, of the Indian Section, Victoria and Albert Museum, all of whom read the manuscript and made many useful suggestions. I have also received unstinted help from Miss P. Edwards and Mr F. C. Sawyer of the Botanical and Zoological Libraries at the British Museum (Natural History), as well as from the Librarian of the India Office Library and his staff, and the Indian Records Section of the Commonwealth Relations Office.

MILDRED ARCHER

May 1961

CONTENTS

ILLUSTRATIONS

vii

PLATE 8

Glory tree (*Clerodendron squamatum*). Wellesley Collection (NHD 18. f. 68). By an Indian artist from the Calcutta Botanic Garden, *c.* 1800

PLATE 9

Indian gerbils (*Tatera indica*). Buchanan Collection (NHD 3. No. 511). By Haludar, an Indian artist employed by the Barrackpore Menagerie, *c.* 1804–5

PLATE 10

Crab-eating macaques (*Macaca irus*). Buchanan Collection (NHD 3. No. 493). By Haludar, an Indian artist employed by the Barrackpore Menagerie, *c.* 1804–5

PLATE 11

Castor-oil tree (*Ricinis communis*). Wellesley Collection (NHD 21. f. 29). By an Indian artist from the Calcutta Botanic Garden, *c.* 1800

PLATE 12

Water melon (*Citrullus vulgaris*). Chinese Drawings (NHD 42. f. 1). By a Chinese artist, probably in Sumatra, *c.* 1808

PLATE 13

Mountain ebony (*Bauhinia diphylla*). Wellesley Collection (NHD 14. f. 99). By an Indian artist from the Calcutta Botanic Garden, *c.* 1800

PLATE 14

Pied-crested cuckoo (*Clamator jacobinus*). Heyne Collection (NHD 1. No. 47). By an Indian artist from south India, *c.* 1793–1813

PLATE 15

Sweet basil (*Ocimum americanum*). Balsam pear (*Momordica charantia*). Wellesley Collection (NHD 18. f. 17 and NHD 21. f. 41). By an Indian artist from the Calcutta Botanic Garden, *c.* 1800

PLATE 16

Malabar glory lily (*Gloriosa superba*). Purple mountain ebony (*Bauhinia purpurea*). Wellesley Collection (NHD 14. ff. 50 and 98). By an Indian artist from the Calcutta Botanic Garden, *c.* 1800

Illustrations

ix

INTRODUCTION

※ i ※

THE COMPANY'S LIBRARY

IN 1801 the Directors of the Honourable East India Company founded a public depository at their House in Leadenhall Street, London, for the miscellaneous material which had been accumulating with them for some years. The depository consisted of a Museum (a 'Cabinet of Natural and Artificial Products') for specimens and objects, and a Library for manuscripts, books and drawings (Plate 25). When the existence of this institution became known, quantities of natural history material began to arrive and the Company steadily built up a large collection of natural history drawings. Private individuals presented their collections, and Company servants on special assignments regularly forwarded the fruits of their researches. Indeed, as ship after ship docked and freight was unloaded, the Day Books of the Library began to include some interesting details.

1802. June 2nd. Three Chests containing a Collection of Insects Shells, Minerals and other objects of Natural History, made at Ceylon by M. Jonville, accompanied by a Memoir in French and Sundry Drawings. Recd from the Baggage Warehouse. It is understood the above was sent as a Present to the Honble Company.

1808. August 24th. Recd from the Examiner's Office, per *Castle Eden*, 26 Drawings of birds and 2 of tortoises, transmitted from Bengal by desire of Dr John Fleming for the Library.

1813. June 7th. Received from the Baggage Warehouse a case pr Ship Surry containing Dr Roxburgh's Drawings & Descriptions of Indian Plants. 132 Sheets of Draws/137 Desc. No. 1833 to 1922 incl. Copies of these despatched on the Honble. Cos. Ship Bengal in 1809. No. 2101 to 2150 Inclusive.

Through presentations of this type, the Company had accumulated by 1859 the finest collection in the country of both drawings and specimens relating to India and South East Asia. All specimens and many drawings were later transferred to other institutions, but the India Office Library (as the Company's Library has been called since 1858) retained a representative selection of the Company's natural history drawings, and to these, additions have been made from time to time (Notes I and II, pages 63–5).

I

Private Individuals as Natural Historians

The collections in the India Office Library fall into two categories: those made by private individuals for their own enjoyment or in satisfaction of their interests; and those which were the work of official naturalists employed for scientific purposes. Between these two groups it is sometimes difficult to distinguish—so thorough and scholarly were certain private collectors, so enthusiastic and lively were certain officials. In general, however, the two types of collector are markedly distinct, for each was governed by different motives, and their collections took separate forms. It will be convenient to consider first the collections made by private individuals.

Private collectors were characterized by infectious enthusiasm and the interests which they had acquired either before leaving Britain or during their sojourn in the East. In England and Scotland, the late eighteenth and early nineteenth centuries had seen great activity in this field. A knowledge of the subject was considered part of a liberal education, and although the scientific specialization of today was less widespread, numerous men and women found time for 'natural philosophy' and a serious study of natural history in its various branches. Their enquiries were helped by the lavishly illustrated books which were produced at this time, the beautiful plates being both a model for amateurs and a challenge to scientific draughtsmanship. Moreover, 'the cult of the picturesque' had awakened the eyes of British observers to the beauties of nature and had quickened in them the desire to record on paper the more curious and vivid aspects of the visible scene. As a consequence, many natural historians paid as careful attention to the sensitive recording of specimens as to their actual collection, and the result was not only a plethora of dried plants and insects and the skins of birds and animals but a series of paintings which made delicate and valuable contributions to British art and science.

When these private enquirers proceeded to India and the East, they were excited to a degree by the birds, flowers, animals and insects which met their delighted eyes. 'What a vast field lies open to the botanist in that boundless country! How little do we know', wrote a Company servant in the early years of the nineteenth century. 'How many unemployed individuals are there, whose leisure hours might be agreeably, usefully and profitably employed in this pursuit! . . . Great God, how wonderful, how manifold are Thy works! In wisdom Thou hast made them all; the earth is full of Thy riches!'[1] The form and brilliance of the many strange creatures and flowers aroused greater enthusiasm than the humbler and less flamboyant species of English woods and fields, and in the letters and journals of the period there are constant descriptions in graceful prose of new sights, so many of which stabbed the eye with their beauty.

James Forbes, for example, derived much happiness during his solitary life from 1765 to 1784 in Western India from watching the strange birds in his garden and making careful descriptions of their appearances and habits:

The baya, or bottle-nested sparrow [he wrote], is remarkable for its pendant nest, brilliant plumage, and uncommon sagacity. These birds are found in most parts of Hindostan; in shape they resemble the sparrow, as also in the brown feathers of the back and wings; the head and breast are of a bright yellow, and in the rays of a tropical sun have a splendid appearance, when flying by thousands in the same grove; they make a chirping noise, but have no song; they associate in large communities; and cover extensive clumps of palmyras, acacias, and date trees, with their nests. These are formed in a very ingenious manner, by long grass woven together in the shape of a bottle, with the neck hanging downwards, and suspended by the other end to the extremity of a flexible branch, the more effectively to secure the eggs and young brood from serpents, monkeys, squirrels, their most deadly enemy, and from birds of prey. These nests contain several apartments, appropriated to different purposes: in one the hen performs the office of incubation; another, consisting of a little thatched roof, and covering a perch, without a bottom, is occupied by the male, who with his chirping note cheers the female during her maternal duties. The Hindoos are very fond of these birds, for their docility and sagacity: when young they teach them to fetch and carry; and at the time the young women resort to the public fountains, their lovers instruct the baya to pluck the tica, or golden ornament, from the forehead of their favourite, and bring it to their expecting master.[2]

Captain Smith, a military engineer with a flair for sketching, made a note in his diary about the *bauhinea*. While taking a lonely walk in the cold weather

---

[1] Preface to an anonymous collection of flower drawings made in India during the first fifteen years of the century. British Museum (Natural History), Botany Department.

[2] J. Forbes, *Oriental Memoirs* (London, 1813), ii, 33.

of 1828 along the river bank at Kara, where his budgerow had tied up for the night, his attention

was attracted by a tree about the size of an apple tree and covered with a profusion of large rose-coloured blossoms, emitting such a delicious perfume as scented the air for a considerable distance around. The flowers were single, and about two and a half inches in diameter with five petals of a pale rose colour, shaded with deep crimson in the centre and streaked with a yet deeper shade; pistil a light pea green, and five stamens of a pale rose with yellow anthers:—perfume highly fragrant. The leaves are two lobed, of a dark pea green, nearly circular, and about three inches diameter with a deep notch at the top.[1]

Maria Graham, the sister of the Professor of Botany at Edinburgh, was yet another keen amateur naturalist who during her visit to India from 1809 to 1811 noted many subjects that excited her interest. While staying in Ceylon she wrote:

I saw in the forest innumerable trees and plants which were new to me, among which I was delighted to find the pitcher-plant, *Nepenthes distillatoria*, or, as it is here called, the monkey cup. It creeps along the ground, and is mostly found in sandy soils; the flower grows in a spike, and is as little attractive in its appearance as the common dock. The horn or cup grows at the end of the leaf, from which it is separated by a tendril of five or six inches long; it contains, when full, about two gills of water of an excellent pure taste: whether it is dew, or a secretion from the plant, I do not know. A circular cover to the cup flies open when it is nearly at its full growth, and shuts again when it is filled with water. The country people say that, when the monkeys are in want of water, they seek for this plant and drink its contents.[2]

She was also interested in insects. While in Calcutta she describes how when returning from the racecourse after sunset, she saw

some of the trees on the esplanade so covered with the fire-fly, as to appear like pyramids of light. This beautiful little insect is about a fourth of an inch in length; its body and wings are of a dark ash-colour; the luminous part is that immediately under the tail, and occupies about one-third of the body; it is not constantly bright, but the insect seems to have the power of becoming luminous at pleasure.[3]

[1] R. Smith, 'Pictorial Journal of Travels in Hindustan from 1828 to 1833' (MS. Victoria and Albert Museum, I.M. 15–1915), 207.

[2] M. Graham, *Journal of a Residence in India* (Edinburgh, 1812), 104–5.

[3] *Ibid.*, 147.

Plants, insects and birds, however, were not the only sources of attraction. Captain Gold, a young officer of the Royal Regiment of Artillery, was fascinated by flying foxes, a picture of which he included in his *Oriental Drawings* in 1806.

On a first view of these singular animals, from the harpy-like appearance of their wings, the fancy naturally occurs that they have made their escape from the infernal regions.

The Flying-fox, as it is termed by the British, from the similarity of its head, skin, and even smell, to the reddish fox, is found in the Mysore, in the Carnatic, and no doubt in the adjoining countries, as well as in the islands of the Indian Ocean. Though certainly of the bat specie, they differ from the common one not only in the vastness of their size, but also from their facing the sun and roosting upon lofty trees, instead of frequenting the solitary haunts of darkness. If they by chance alight on the ground, it is difficult, from their want of legs, to raise themselves again into the air; and from the same cause when at rest on a tree, instead of perching as the bird, they hang by the claws at the extremity of the body, with their heads suspended downwards.[1]

Passages of this kind suggest the mixed excitement and curiosity with which many of the British viewed for the first time the natural history of the East. But vivid description was not enough. Just as their counterparts at home had systematically collected specimens and at the same time drawn them and acquired illustrated books, so in the East these lively individuals were keen to collect specimens and also paintings. Creatures might be stuffed, varnished or preserved in spirits, plants could be pressed and dried, but paintings were needed to show the specimen in its living shape and with its true colours. Drawings, in fact, served not only as a sentimental reminder of excited reactions to new sights, but were a definite contribution to science for they could be sent or taken to England to help identify and classify specimens. They were by far the most accurate means of recording natural history specimens and the easiest to store and transmit. Many collections therefore were made and some reached the India Office Library.

[1] C. Gold, *Oriental Drawings* (London, 1806). Note to picture of 'Flying-foxes and Banyan Tree'.

❧ iii ❧

PRIVATE COLLECTORS IN INDIA

Collections of natural history drawings by private individuals can be divided into two groups: those which were made in India; and those which came from the Company's possessions farther east.

Of those made in India, the earliest drawings possessed by the Library were executed by Indian draughtsmen for Dr James Kerr (1738–1782), a Company Surgeon on the Bengal Establishment from 1770 to 1782. After working as a ship's surgeon from 1763 to 1772, he appears to have spent his service in Bihar and Bengal (he was in Dacca in 1774), and while there to have interested himself in subjects such as the cultivation of opium and lac. A small collection of his botanical papers are in the Library (MSS. Eur. E.11), among them four water-colour drawings illustrating his articles on a 'New Plant from which the Terra Japonica of the shops is extracted', on the lac insect which thrives on the *Palas* tree, and on a 'New & Singular Plant, the . . . Burrum Chundalli'. Kerr was fascinated by the moving leaves of this plant and concludes his note (pages 69–70):

It is no wonder that this strange plant should become an Object of Superstition, among an Illiterate people; On their day called Sunichur (Saturday) they cut off two lobes at the instant they approach together, & beat them up with the Tongue of an Owl: with this composition the Lover touches his favorite Mistress, to make her comply with his wishes!

The Marquis Wellesley

The finest private collection in the India Office Library, however, is that of the Marquis Wellesley (1760–1842). This was made while he was Governor-General of Fort William from 1798 to 1805 and consists of two thousand, six hundred and sixty folios of natural history paintings depicting plants, birds, mammals, insects and fishes. (NHD 10–36, Frontispiece, Plates 1, 6, 7, 8, 11, 13, 15, 16, 20.) Wellesley had unusual opportunities for amassing a great collection. As a result of his important office he regularly received presents of rare flowers, birds or animals. Some were sent by Company servants from all over India, others were brought by visiting ships or travellers from further east—from Malaya, Penang, Sumatra, the Moluccas

6

PLATE I Shoe flower (*Hibiscus rosa-sinensis*)
Wellesley Collection

and even Australia; while as Governor-General he met everyone in Calcutta who was interested in natural history, whether resident or visitor. Moreover, at this time the Presidency town contained a number of keen and learned natural historians who continually met each other and exchanged ideas and information (see page 22).

It is not surprising then that a great collection was amassed. Many drawings depict birds, animals and plants which Wellesley had received as gifts, and some bear inscriptions recording details. A cheetah 'drawn from life' 'was found in the Palace of Tippoo Sultan at Seringapatam, 1799' (NHD 32. f. 3). A picture of a hunting lynx is described, 'From life in possession of Marquis Wellesley.' 'This animal was given me by Rajah Mitter Jeet Singh, a Zemindar of Bahar . . . W. 1802' (f. 7). A picture of a leopard is inscribed, 'From life, sent from the Coast of Malabar' (NHD 33. f. 2). A number of drawings came from farther afield, from Malacca, Penang and the Moluccas. These must have aroused great interest at the time since only a few years previously, as a result of Napoleon's occupation of the Netherlands, the Company had seized a number of French and Dutch possessions in the Far East. Malacca, for example, was taken from the Dutch in 1795 so that it could not be used as a base for attacks on British shipping. As a result of these conquests British administrators proceeded to these areas, and following the practice of other civilians not only began to investigate the local flora and fauna but recruited local artists—the Chinese—to make drawings of them. Some of these drawings appear to have been despatched to Wellesley and his collection thus contains some of the first drawings from these areas.

Not all his drawings, however, were of presents, for other pictures reflect his contacts with fellow enthusiasts who had chanced to fill gaps in his collection. Lord Valentia visited Wellesley in Calcutta in 1803 during his tour of the East and gave him some bird paintings. Captain Hardwicke of the Bengal Artillery (see page 8) also presented him with drawings of birds from the Himalayas. In addition certain pictures in Wellesley's collection are copies of originals made for Captain Hardwicke, while others are based on drawings brought back by Dr Buchanan from Nepal and Mysore in 1801 and 1802.

Such drawings are in the main exceptional, for the rest appear to have been made expressly for Wellesley by Calcutta painters from specimens which he either acquired locally or saw growing in the Botanic Garden. An orchid was found 'growing on a mango tree in Mr Dodwell's Garden' (NHD 13. f. 85). Other plants were from up-country stations in Bengal—from Rangpur, Dinajpur or Midnapore—the drawings being carefully inscribed with their Bengali, Urdu or Hindi names. Notes were also sometimes added recording information given by local inhabitants concerning their economic or social uses: 'The grass used by Hindoos in their worship' (NHD 10. f. 111); 'The oil much used by the Natives on their food' (NHD 15. f. 95); 'The best bow-strings made from this plant' (NHD 15. f. 58); 'The light pith used to make Toys for Children' (NHD 19. f. 88). In this way through personal curiosity and the help of enthusiastic friends, Wellesley was able to build up a great collection which reflected the cultured interests of an eighteenth-century nobleman.

Lord Clive

While Wellesley was amassing drawings in Calcutta, Lord Clive (later the first Earl Powis) was making another collection in Madras. Edward Clive (1754–1839), eldest son of the famous Robert Clive, was Governor of Madras from 1798 to 1803, and during these years collected several volumes of natural history paintings from South India, some of which were sold in 1956 at Sotheby's by his descendant, Lord Powis. At this sale the India Office Library acquired fifteen drawings: three of animals, two of birds, nine of fish and one of a turtle (NHD 44/1–15, Plate 18). These differ in style from the remainder of Clive's collection, and from the inscription 'Malacaw' on two fish drawings it would appear that they were made in Malacca by Chinese painters. The two bird pictures also resemble those from Malacca in Wellesley's collection, and just as some of the newly arrived British adminis-trators had supplied Wellesley with drawings, it seems likely that one or more of them may have made similar presents to Clive.

Major-General Thomas Hardwicke

One of the greatest collectors of natural history drawings in India was Major-General Hardwicke of the Bengal Artillery (1755–1835). He entered the service in 1778, fought in the Second and Third Mysore Wars and returned to the Bengal Presidency in 1793. He took part in the Second Rohilla War in 1794 and from 1797 to 1803 was based on Cawnpore. After three years' furlough in England he returned to Bengal in 1806, and from 1808 to 1811 was a member of the Military Board before going on leave again from 1811 to 1815. From 1816 to 1818 he was once again a member of the Military Board and acting Commandant of the Artillery at Dumdum. After two more years' leave he became Commandant from 1820 to 1822 and eventually retired from India in 1823.

Throughout his career Hardwicke was interested in natural history and managed to combine the collecting of specimens and drawings with his military duties. From 1796 he was a keen member of the Asiatic Society of Bengal, becoming its Vice-President from 1820 to 1822, and during his years at Dumdum he was able to share the enthusiastic researches of a little group of naturalists in Calcutta (see page 22). He employed artists, both Indian and British, to draw the specimens of flowers, birds, mammals and insects, which he collected, and by the time he retired he had a vast number. Fifteen hundred of his drawings are now in the British Museum (Natural History), but they are only part of the original collection, for he was continually giving drawings to his friends. Forbes Royle (see page 25) availed himself of Hardwicke's paintings and refers to 'ten volumes of drawings made in the plains of Northern India, and also while travelling nearly thirty years ago in the Himalayas'.[1] J. E. Gray, who used many of Hardwicke's drawings in his *Illustrations of Indian Zoology*, notes how they 'were made upon the spot and chiefly from living specimens of Animals—executed by English and Native Artists, constantly employed for this purpose under his own immediate superintendence'.[2]

Ninety-six drawings of Indian birds which are in the India Office Library (NHD 39) were almost certainly part of Hardwicke's collection and may well be paintings given by him to a friend. The paper has 1794 and 1801 watermarks while Urdu inscriptions on the drawings record that the specimens were collected in Kumaon, Srinagar and Betul, areas which Hardwicke had

[1] J. F. Royle, *Illustrations of the Botany and Other Branches of the Natural History of the Himalayan Mountains and of the Flora of Cashmere* (London, 1833–39), i, 3.

[2] J. E. Gray and T. Hardwicke, *Illustrations of Indian Zoology* (London, 1830–35), Preface.

explored after the Rohilla War of 1794. Two folios of bird drawings in Wellesley's collection (NHD 29. ff. 80 and 87) are inscribed as depicting specimens from Srinagar, and it is almost certain that Wellesley acquired these from Hardwicke, for no other collector was active in this area at the time. It will be noted that the style of these two folios is identical with some in the volume of ninety-six drawings under discussion, while the inscriptions are also similar in form (cf. NHD 29. f. 80 and NHD 39. f. 43). On stylistic grounds other folios in the Wellesley collection (e.g. NHD 29. ff. 47 and 48) would also appear to have come from Hardwicke. It is amusing to notice that Horsfield wrote 'fancy portrait' on one of these drawings (NHD 29. f. 48), while the expert at the Natural History Museum, to whom the ninety-six drawings were shown in 1891, dismissed them as 'nonsense birds'. Apparently Hardwicke's artists who made these paintings were not amenable to British scientific methods, and perhaps because of their inaccuracy these particular drawings were given away.

Dr John Leyden

A few years later a small collection of natural history drawings was made by Dr John Leyden (1775–1811), probably in Calcutta (NHD 40). Unlike other natural history material in the Library, it is in oriental style. The paintings are in gouache and bound together in pairs in a *muraqqa'* in traditional Mughal manner. The artist was clearly given subjects to paint such as vegetables, which he had never attempted before, and he was probably told to render them as realistically as possible. As a result the drawings have neither the decorative quality of Mughal painting, nor the naturalism of drawings in western style. The lines are hesitant and weak and often wrongly drawn so that the artist has tried to cover them with chinese white. They illustrate, in fact, the difficulties which many Indian artists may have experienced when trying to adjust their Indian styles to British tastes. The volume was part of Leyden's oriental library which was acquired by the Company in 1824.

John Leyden, a young Scottish doctor, reached Madras in 1803 and was attached to Colonel Colin MacKenzie as naturalist and assistant surgeon to the Mysore survey (see page 38). As a result of ill health he was sent to Penang in 1805, where he formed a lasting friendship with Stamford Raffles and his wife, Olivia (page 15). In 1806 he was posted to Calcutta as Professor of

Hindustani at Wellesley's Fort William College, and later as Judge of Twenty-four Parganas near Calcutta, Commissioner of the Court of Requests and Assay Master of the Mint. In 1811 he accompanied the Java expedition but died two days after the fall of Cornelis. He was a brilliant linguist and was interested in natural history and antiquities, a contemporary describing him as 'a curious mixture of the apothecary, poet and scholar'.

Brian Houghton Hodgson

Enthusiasm for natural history persisted in India during much of the nineteenth century, and two other collections in the India Office Library recall the contributions of private collectors at a slightly later date. Five pictures of mammals (NHD 5, Nos. 765–9) are from the collection of Brian Houghton Hodgson (1800–1894), who had entered the Company's service in 1818 and spent many years in Nepal. From 1820 to 1829 he was Assistant Resident at Katmandu, from 1829 to 1831 Acting Resident and from 1833 to 1844 Resident. During this time he made a great collection of Tibetan and Sanskrit manuscripts, and of geographical and ethnological material, most of which has come to the India Office Library. But he was also a keen natural historian. On reaching Katmandu he had taken up snipe shooting to fill his leisure hours, but soon became so interested in the birds and animals which he saw that he engaged hunters to shoot and trap other and rarer species for him. He carefully weighed, measured and described the specimens, more especially birds and quadrupeds, and for many years employed three Indian assistants. 'I have three native artists,' he wrote to his sister, 'always employed in drawing from nature. I possess a live tiger, a wild sheep, a wild goat, four bears, three civets and three score of our beautiful pheasants. A rare menagerie. And my drawings now amount to two thousand.'[1] After his retirement he lived in Darjeeling until 1858 in order to continue these studies. He eventually collected nine thousand five hundred and twelve pictures of birds, nine hundred and three of mammals and eighty-four of reptiles all of which were presented by him to the British Museum and the Zoological Society. From so rich a collection five drawings are admittedly a poor share. They serve, however, to remind us of Hodgson's great contribution to natural

[1] W. W. Hunter, *Life of Brian Houghton Hodgson* (London, 1896), 79.

history, and the Library must perhaps be grateful that as the result of chance it possesses any at all. The drawings appear to have been sent to Dr Horsfield, the Keeper of the India House Museum, as illustrations to articles, and they remained with the Library when the Museum was dispersed.

Edward Blyth

Another collection of eighteen bird paintings was presented by Edward Blyth (1810–1873). Blyth had started life as a druggist in Tooting, but his business did not thrive, for all his energy was poured into his hobby of natural history. By 1840 the Museum of the Asiatic Society in Calcutta was in disorder, for the honorary office-bearers had been unable to cope with the stream of specimens presented by collectors such as Hodgson, Cantor and McClelland. In 1840 the Society applied to the Company for a grant to provide the Museum with a permanent Curator. Blyth obtained this post in 1841 and he remained in Calcutta for twenty-one years.

Under his direction, the collections were re-arranged and greatly extended. He made numerous friends, such as Dr Jerdon, Colonel Phayre of Burma and Captain Tickell of Chaibasa, who sent him specimens from all over India and the East Indies. He was thus able to build up for the Asiatic Society's Museum in India the best collection of birds outside Europe or North America, and indeed can perhaps be regarded as the founder of scientific ornithology in India. He carefully catalogued the collection, helped many ornithologists, such as Jerdon and Jardine, wrote numerous papers and, above all, presented regular monthly reports to the Asiatic Society, a practice, Hugh Strickland remarked, 'which the curators of European Museums would do well to imitate'.[1]

For field work, however, Blyth had little opportunity, though he made occasional expeditions into the countryside. It is related that on one of these expeditions to Lucknow in 1856, soon after the British had deposed the King of Oudh, he was persuaded by a speculator friend to purchase the bulk of the Royal Menagerie for a mere trifle. He found himself the owner of eighteen tigers at £2 a head, as well as a leopard, a bear, two cheetahs, three caracals, two rhinoceroses and a giraffe. Owing to difficulties of transport and several

---

[1] W. Jardine, *Memoirs of Hugh Edwin Strickland* (London, 1858), 269.

casualties en route, however, he made no profit, although he succeeded in selling one tiger in England for £140.

While in Calcutta, Blyth sent specimens to the Company's Museum, and between 1843 and 1855 seven consignments arrived. The paintings in the Library (NHD 8, Nos. 1296–1313) were presented in 1863 after his retirement, and they include at least one type drawing. They portray birds not only from India but from Nepal, Bhutan, Tenasserim, Singapore and Australia.

Raja Serfagee of Tanjore

Such collections were all made by Europeans. There remains, however, one further collection (NHD 7, Nos. 1001–1116), perhaps the strangest of all, and this was almost certainly made not by a Company servant but by an Indian. It depicts birds, mammals, fishes, reptiles and shellfish and was made in about 1802. It is accompanied by notes in broken English. In 1888 when the Library's printed catalogue was compiled, the origin of this collection was apparently overlooked and it was called the 'Mysore Collection'. Tanjore, however, is frequently mentioned in the inscriptions, as also is 'the palace'. A picture of a bird is inscribed, 'She has laid an Egg after it came to my Palace'; and another, 'This bird was lately brought to Tanjore from Hyderabad.' Such notes would suggest that this collection is in fact not a 'Mysore Collection' but 'The Natural Products of Hindostan, painted under the direction of the Rajah of Tanjore', two folio volumes of which were presented in 1807 to the Company by Mr Benjamin Torin, Resident of Tanjore from 1801 to 1803.[1] Horsfield had referred to this 'Tanjore Collection' in his catalogue of the Museum's mammalia. Of Tanjore volumes there is now no trace in the Library, and it therefore seems almost certain that these drawings were remounted about 1880 and erroneously entitled 'Mysore Collection'.

If these are indeed the paintings 'made under the direction of the Rajah of Tanjore', they gain greatly in interest. Raja Serfagee of Tanjore, who had been re-instated on the throne by the British in 1798, had been educated by a certain Mr Swartz and the Rev. W. Geriche of the Lutheran Mission. The comments in this volume, written in a neat copper-plate hand on carefully ruled pencil lines, are exactly what we would expect from this young Raja.

[1] See *Court Book*, Vol. 116, 311.

A shell is described as 'a kind of Sea-Worm-cage' (No. 1103). The following note accompanies a Royal Tiger (No. 1035).

This kind of Tygers is more strength than all the Animals and its nature without Provocation is fierceness and Cruel. No Mercy is to be expected from this Bruit which indiscriminate fury and tears in pieces Every Animals He met with. He is generally known to lurk near the places where He has an Opportunity to Chace His prey. We understood that the Tygers in Mysore or on the west part Country is 9 feets long from His snout to the tail and 5½ feets heighth, but Tyger drawn in this Picture was got in the eastern part of the Country and its Eight feets long from snout to the tail and 4 feet in heigth but it has been taken when it was young and continually confined in a strongest wooden Cage. The prey which now usually gives to this Animal once a day Twenty seers of Mutton at 12 o'clock in the morning and some time the Sickness of Rumatism will frequently happen to it which will be cured by giving 3 fanams weight musk with Mutton. If this Animal is eat too much He will be indocility but if it was given a Small prey He will be very anger & be cruel & roar too much.

The book opens with twenty-five different species of falcon and hawk, probably belonging to the Raja himself, each bird being shown on a brocade cushion or tasselled perch (Plate 17).

If Raja Serfagee of Tanjore was the author of this collection, then the drawings are significant in showing how the enthusiastic study of natural history, and the collecting of paintings, so fashionable with the British, had been communicated to a young Indian prince through western education.

❧ iv ❧

PRIVATE COLLECTORS IN SOUTH EAST ASIA

If India was the greatest of the Company's territories in the East, it was not, however, its sole possession. While, therefore, the natural history of the continent bulked large in the drawings which reached London, other regions further east also made their contributions. The most important were the Malay peninsula, Sumatra and Java. During the Napoleonic Wars, when Britain captured many French and Dutch possessions in South East Asia, the East Indies began to attract enthusiastic attention, and the greatest investigator to form a private collection there was Sir Stamford Raffles (1781–1826).

Sir Stamford Raffles

Sailing for the East in 1805, Raffles was already imbued with an irrepressible enthusiasm for natural history. He pursued this hobby in spite of illness, family tragedies, administrative worries and official hostility, and found peace of mind in investigating the natural life around him and in writing happy letters to scholars and fellow enthusiasts. Among his discoveries was an astonishing flower, later called the *Rafflesia Arnoldi* after Raffles himself and his friend, Dr Arnold. In July 1818 he wrote from Southern Sumatra to the Duchess of Somerset,

The most important discovery throughout our journey was made at this place; this was a gigantic flower, of which I can hardly attempt to give any thing like a just description. It is perhaps the largest and most magnificent flower in the world, and is so distinct from every other flower, that I know not to what I can compare it—its dimensions will astonish you—it measured across from the extremity of the petals rather more than a yard, the nectarium was nine inches wide, and as deep; estimated to contain a gallon and a half of water, and the weight of the whole flower fifteen pounds. . . . The inside of the cup is of an intense purple, and more or less densely yellow, with soft flexible spines of the same colour: towards the mouth, it is marked with numerous depressed spots of the purest white, contrasting strongly with the purple of the surrounding substance, which is considerably elevated on the lower side. The petals are of a brick-red, with numerous pustular spots of a lighter colour. . . . If I am successful in obtaining a draftsman, your Grace shall have a perfect representation of it. I have made a very rough sketch of it myself, but it is not in that state that I could venture to present it. It seems to be a flower unknown to most of the natives, as well as to naturalists; its colours red, yellow, and purple, and most brilliant.[1]

A few years later in 1823, while engaged in drawing up a constitution and a code of law for Singapore, he wrote to the Duchess about yet another amazing plant.

We have recently discovered a companion for my great flower, in a noble Orchideous plant, which will shortly be described by Mr Finlayson and my friend Dr Wallich, the latter of whom has taken several growing specimens to Calcutta, in the hope of getting them to England. It grows parasitically on rocks, or roots, in several of the Islands in the Straits of Malacca, and the stems are as thick as a man's wrist, and from six to ten feet long, without branches, at the extremity of which they produce abundance of

---

1 S. Raffles, *Memoir of the Life and Public Services of Sir Thomas Stamford Raffles* (London, 1830), 316.

leaves. But the wonder is, its magnificent inflorescence, which forms an erect spike *six feet high*, with upwards of one hundred large-spreading brown and white chequered fragrant flowers, between two and three inches in diameter.[1]

But Raffles did not stop at descriptions. Although not officially connected with natural history, he was no dilettante, but possessed a professional scholar's respect for exact knowledge and scientific data. And wherever he was stationed, he organized a survey of natural history as well as a systematic collection of specimens. Abdullah, one of his Malay clerks, has left a description of his activity while in Malacca from 1810 to 1811.

He kept four persons on wages, each in their peculiar departments; one to go to the forests in search of various kinds of leaves, flowers, fungi, pulp and such like products. Another he sent to collect all kinds of flies, grasshoppers, bees in all their varieties, as well as scorpions, centipedes and such like, giving him needles as well as pins with a box to stick the creatures therein. Another he sent with a basket to seek for coral, shells, oysters, mussels, cockles and such like; also fishes of various species; and another to collect animals, such as birds, jungle fowl, deer, stags, mouse-deers and so forth. Then he had a large book with thick paper, whose use was for the keeping of the leaves and flowers. And when he could not put them there, he had a Chinese Macao painter, who was good at painting fruit and flowers to the life, these he set him to copy. Again, he kept a barrel full of arrack, or brandy, and when he had got snakes, scorpions, centipedes, or such like, he would put them into it till they were dead, before putting them in bottles.[2]

After the conquest of Java by the British in 1811, order had scarcely been restored before Raffles organized a survey of the island's natural history in conjunction with Dr Horsfield, a scientist already employed by the Dutch. In 1818, he returned from England as Lieutenant-Governor of Sumatra, and at once began to investigate the natural history of the island. New collections of specimens and drawings were formed and he continued to add to them on an even more extensive scale in Singapore from 1822 to 1823. Abdullah has described the collection when it came to be packed.

There were many thousands of specimens of animals whose carcasses had been taken out but stuffed like life. There were also two or three trunks full of birds in thousands

---

[1] S. Raffles, *ibid.*, 535.
[2] C. E. Wurtzburg, *Raffles of the Eastern Isles* (London, 1954), 113.

and of various species, and all stuffed. There were also several hundred bottles of different sizes filled with snakes, scorpions and worms of different kinds. The bottles were filled with gin to prevent corruption. The animals were thus like life. There were also two boxes filled with coral of a thousand kinds; also shells, mussels and bivalves of different species. On all these articles stated above he placed a value greater than gold, and he was constantly coming in to see that nothing was hurt or broken.[1]

And in addition to these specimens was a great collection of over two thousand drawings.

As a result of these systematic investigations, Raffles was constantly despatching specimens and drawings to England, and in a letter to Marsden, the orientalist, from Bencoolen in June 1820, he describes one such consignment.

As there was no chance of a direct opportunity, I have sent by the London duplicates, and even more complete sets of the quadrupeds and birds than those sent by the Mary, numbered, named, and ticketed, so as to correspond with my catalogues. I am at this moment superintending a complete set of the drawings, to be forwarded by the present opportunity, *via* Calcutta. I fear there will hardly be time for completing the duplicates of the catalogue of birds. My writers are now engaged upon it, and I will do my best to send it by the present conveyance. . . . We are now busy in arranging the reptiles and crabs, of which we have a very large collection.[2]

Crate after crate was despatched in this way to London, yet of these collections, so carefully amassed, few have survived, all those made in his last years being destroyed in 1824 when his boat, the *Fame*, caught fire. The collections which reached England are now preserved in the British Museum (Natural History), but the India Office Library possesses a single collection of water-colour drawings of birds (NHD 4, Nos. 537–665) made in Sumatra probably in 1820, perhaps the very ones mentioned in Raffles' letter of June 1820.

William Marsden

Another collection of drawings from Sumatra was made by Raffles' friend, William Marsden (1754–1836). Although primarily interested in history and languages, Marsden was also a keen natural historian and in close touch

[1] C. E. Wurtzburg, *ibid.*, 652.
[2] S. Raffles, *op. cit.*, 453.

with British scientists of his day. He served with the East India Company at Bencoolen in Sumatra from 1771 to 1779, where, as he says in his autobiography,

My curiosity being ever awake to the novelty of objects around me, I omitted no opportunities of making remarks on, and enquiries concerning, whatever was striking in the productions of the country, or peculiar in the manners of the natives.[1]

His interests, like those of many of his contemporaries, were quite extraordinarily broad, and in the preface to his *History of Sumatra* (published in 1783) he explains that his aim is

sincerely and conscientiously to add the small portion in my power, to the general knowledge of the age; to throw some glimmering light on the path of the naturalist, and more especially to furnish those philosophers, whose labors have been directed to the investigation of the history of Man, with facts to serve as data in their reasonings, which are often rendered nugatory, and not seldom ridiculous, by assuming as truths, the misconceptions, or wilful impositions of travellers.[2]

Marsden's collection consists of thirty-five drawings (NHD 1, Nos. 1–31 and NHD 2, Nos. 285, 300–2) portraying animals, birds, fishes and shells. These pictures were acquired from various friends in Sumatra between the years 1784 and 1808, when he was collecting illustrations for a new and more lavish edition of his *History of Sumatra*. He wrote concerning the year 1808:

My chief literary occupation about this time was in preparing a new edition of the History of Sumatra, which had been for many years out of print. During the interval, I had taken every opportunity of collecting additional information, as well as drawings of animals and plants, views of the country, and other subjects, by means of which, and some corrections, I was enabled to improve the work considerably.[3]

Eleven of the twenty-seven plates in the magnificent third edition of his book were engraved from these pictures. Several drawings were made by 'W. Bell', probably Dr William Bell, a Company Surgeon who was in Sumatra in 1792 and died there in the same year. Two others were provided by de

[1] W. Marsden, *A Brief Memoir of the Life and Writings of the late William Marsden, written by himself* (London, 1838), 15.
[2] W. Marsden, *History of Sumatra* (London, 1783), vi–viii.
[3] W. Marsden, *Memoir*, 139.

Jonville (see page 34), while others were by Chinese painters, for the engravings from them are lettered, 'Sinensis delt' (Plate 2). It was fitting that Mrs Marsden should present her husband's pictures to the Library, for she herself was the eldest daughter of Sir Charles Wilkins, its first Librarian, and she and her sisters had done much to help with the production of the new edition of the *History of Sumatra* (see page 100).

Richard Parry

About the same time as Marsden was at work, Richard Parry, Resident of Sumatra from 1807 to 1811, made a similar collection of paintings. Parry had been in the East since 1793, from 1796 to 1800 as Assistant to the Sub-Treasurer in Calcutta and from 1800 to 1803 as Sub-Treasurer. While in the Presidency capital, Parry, like Wellesley and several other natural historians, probably acquired the habit of collecting drawings made by Indian artists. And it is at this time that he may well have begun to commission the Indian artist, Manu Lal, who appears to have accompanied him to Sumatra and to have made drawings for him there. On returning to England, Parry gave his collection of flowers, birds and animals to the Company, an entry in the Day Book for 26th June 1812 stating that Mr Richard Parry had given two hundred and two drawings of 'Plants and Animals from Sumatra'. The flower paintings were later presented to the Kew Herbarium, but twelve drawings of birds, one of mammals and one of fishes (NHD 2, Nos. 286–99) remain in the Library (Plate 3).

v

OFFICIAL NATURAL HISTORIANS AND THEIR COLLECTIONS IN INDIA

The collections we have so far considered reflect the hobbies of private individuals. We must now examine the work of official naturalists. Many of these were doctors or military engineers. Few had received a specialized training in botany or zoology in England or had had these interests aroused by university teachers. The majority, in fact, had merely pursued natural history as a private interest. They possessed, however, one important advantage: they were trained scientists or mathematicians, and as soon as the Company placed them on special duties connected with natural history they applied the latest and most exacting standards of scientific enquiry. As a result, some of them became expert natural historians. They laid the true foundations of Indian natural history, and their collections account for the greater part of the Library's natural history drawings.

By the end of the eighteenth century the Company, with its shrewd business instincts, had come to realize the economic value of research into the natural history of the East. Although loath to spend money unless some ultimate profit would result, it gradually became convinced that research of this type would eventually yield financial results. Botany, for example, was necessary for experimental horticulture and the conservation of forests. It could help in the development of medicine and many technical processes. And as time went on, the Company's attitude became even broader. A knowledge of natural history was needed in medical schools, and the Company also felt a duty to support scientific research for its own sake and to publish the work of scholars.

Its first official act was the establishment of Botanic Gardens. The largest was near Sibpur on the River Hooghly opposite Fort William, Calcutta (Plate 24). Lieutenant-Colonel Robert Kyd of the Bengal Infantry had already started a private botanic garden here at his country house of Shalimar. He initiated a scheme for the establishment by the Company of an official garden on a plot of land adjoining his own estate. This was officially acquired in 1787 and Kyd became its Honorary Superintendent.[1] After his death in 1793 an official Superintendent, Dr William Roxburgh, was appointed, and the drawings which were produced there under his supervision were to have far-reaching results on natural history drawing in India.

Dr William Roxburgh

Roxburgh had been in India since 1776 and from 1781 had been in charge of a botanic garden at Samalkot, an experimental station in the Madras Presidency where pepper, sappan, tobacco and cardamons were grown.

---

[1] Lt.-Col. R. Kyd, 'Some remarks on the Soil and Cultivation on the Western Side of the River Hoogly'. MSS. Eur. F. 95.

From 1789 until 1793 he was the Company's Botanist in the Carnatic and distinguished himself by studying the flora of the Northern Sircars and the Coromandel Coast. While in the south he had also begun descriptions of Indian flora. He worked methodically, giving a number to each plant and at the same time having a life-size drawing made to which the same number was given. Duplicates of his descriptions and drawings were despatched to the Company, and between 1791 and 1794 about five hundred of these were received in London.

It is during this period that the first of Roxburgh's five drawings, which are still in the Library's collection, were produced. (Home Miscellaneous Series, 375.) In 1791 the Directors had enquired from him concerning the cultivation of hemp and flax, and in February 1793, he sent them his first reply describing a new species of flax and enclosing a drawing. Later, in December, 1794, he sent a second note from Calcutta attaching four further drawings and describing the hemp and flax plants of Bengal 'with the mode of cultivation and manufacture'. Other Roxburgh drawings have since been transferred to the Kew Herbarium, but these five drawings remain.

Roxburgh's task on joining the Botanic Garden was to make an exhaustive survey of India's flora. Although, as in selecting the Coromandel plants, the Company 'with a view to utility' gave preference to the study of 'subjects connected either with medicine, the arts, or manufacturers', it also encouraged 'the admission of new plants, or of such as have hitherto been imperfectly described'. Roxburgh continued to add to his list, and as part of his work he recruited and trained a team of Indian artists to draw every species of plant listed. He followed the plan of Koenig and Banks, whereby specimens were collected and then drawn, the description being made at the same time from the same fresh specimen. When sending his drawings to the Company from South India, Roxburgh had noted, 'The whole of the drawings and descriptions, six or seven excepted, were taken from the living plants, repeatedly examined and corrected during a period of twenty years' constant application to the study of Indian Botany.' The drawings were on folio size sheets, and both plants and dissections were natural size.

This method was continued at the Calcutta Garden for twenty years, and when Roxburgh retired in 1813 a total of two thousand five hundred and forty-two paintings had been made in the south and at Calcutta by his team of Indian artists. They are still in the Sibpur Herbarium bound in thirty-five volumes known as the *Roxburgh Icones*. Duplicates of these drawings made at Sibpur were sent home to the Company, and the Library's Day Books record a constant flow, albeit sometimes interrupted by the loss of a ship.

1811.   Octr. 22d. 100 Drawings and Descriptions of Indian Plants from No. 2001 2100 inclusive, with Seventy four Drawings & 70 sheets of Descriptions of Indian Plants which had been transmitted before by missing ship Bengal from No. 1759 to 1832 inclusive.

1813. June 7th. Received from the Baggage Warehouse a case pr Ship Surry containing Dr Roxburgh's Drawings & Descriptions of Indian Plants. 132 Sheets of Draws / 137 Desc. No. 1833 to 1922 incl. Copies of those despatched on the Honble. Cos. Ship Bengal in 1809. No. 2101 to 2150 Inclusive.

Two hundred and sixty-nine more drawings, Nos. 2151 to 2411, followed in September 1813.

Such drawings were to play a supreme role in later botanical research. Together with their descriptions they formed the basis of the first standard works on Indian botany—the *Hortus Bengalensis* and the *Flora Indica* edited by Carey from Roxburgh's material in 1814 and 1820. They account for almost four hundred plates in Wight's *Icones Plantarum Indiae Orientalis* (1838–1853) while three hundred were also selected by Sir Joseph Banks and published at the Company's expense as *Plants of the Coast of Coromandel* (1795–1820). Their importance, however, greatly exceeds this limited function. Besides providing Roxburgh's successors at the Garden with rigorous standards, they served as models for many important collections of drawings made in Calcutta. At this time there was a keen group of Company servants in the Bengal Presidency. It is clear, for example, from notes on Wellesley's drawings that Company servants in Bengal, such as William Cowper, Charles Crommelin, John Fombelle and John Thornhill, were interested in natural history, raising rare flowers and keeping private menageries. In Calcutta itself there were distinguished men and women such as the Marquis Wellesley and Lady Hastings. There was Hardwicke at Dumdum and a number of Company surgeons, as well as visitors such as Lord Valentia and Maria Graham. Many of these natural historians exchanged information and collected drawings. They may often have gone to the Sibpur Garden to watch the progress of the

Roxburgh Icones and may even have sent their own artists to the Herbarium to copy the official paintings. Such a practice would explain the collection of Dr Michael Cheese (1757–1816), a Company doctor in Calcutta, whose ninety-nine pictures are now in the Reading Public Library. Although some of Cheese's drawings are exact copies of official paintings, they are executed in a crude style quite unlike that of the Company's skilled draughtsmen who worked for Roxburgh, and we can only conclude that perhaps some lesser practitioner was granted access to the Company's collection and allowed to make selected copies. A more common practice, however, may well have been the employment of official artists. In certain cases collectors may have commissioned copies of paintings which interested them or which they wished to send to fellow scholars in England. In the alternative they may have ordered extensive sets. Roxburgh's drawings were certainly repeated and in at least two further cases numbers of copies still exist. Dr John Fleming (1747–1829), a surgeon in Bengal from 1768 to 1813 and a keen botanist, probably used the Garden's team of painters, for among his large collection of drawings, some are exact copies of the *Roxburgh Icones*. One thousand eight hundred and twenty-five of his paintings of Indian plants appear to have found their way to a nobleman's collection in Brussels, and thirteen folio volumes were purchased by the British Museum (Natural History) in 1882. Other copies are in the Wellesley Collection. The Governor-General must either himself have ordered these paintings from the artists at the Calcutta Garden or else have been presented with them by Roxburgh. The drawings were added to the collection which Wellesley had begun to compile for himself and they are now intermixed (Note III, page 65).

Dr Nathaniel Wallich

The tradition of recording specimens by careful drawings established at the Calcutta Garden by Roxburgh was carried on by his successors. From 1813 until 1817 there was a somewhat confused period of administration with a number of officiating Superintendents—H. T. Colebrooke, Francis Buchanan, Nathaniel Wallich, James Hare and Thomas Casey, but the team of painters at the Botanic Garden continued its work without interruption. The Garden itself was also well maintained, and we can estimate how popular was its appeal from an account by the engineer, Captain Smith, who visited it in 1828.

I have already said that the gardens are very extensive containing 600 acres, which is partly laid out in broad grass walks shaded by the luxuriant vegetable productions of the East, and diversified by tanks and other pieces of ornamental water, producing a beautiful variety of interesting scenery. There are several very fine Banyan trees; (*Ficus religiosa*) one in particular from its great size, and numerous pendant branches, and being still a young tree is deserving of notice. The annexed sketch is a faithful representation of it; but a more beautiful illustration of this most magnificent of Nature's works is in the following lines from Milton.

> *There soon they chose*
> *The fig tree, not that kind for fruit renown'd,*
> *But such as at this day to Indians known*
> *In Malabar or Deccan spreads her arms*
> *Branching so broad and long, that in the ground*
> *The bended twigs take root, and daughters grow*
> *About the mother tree, a pillar'd shade*
> *High overarch'd, and echoing walks between;*
> *There oft the Indian herdsman, shunning heat,*
> *Shelters in cool, and tends his pasturing herds*
> *At loop-holes cut thro' thickest shade.*

There is also the sago palm (*Phoenix farinifera*), the plantain, (*Mura paradisaica*), the pawpaw (*Carica papaya*) a fruit much like the melon, the *Urania speciosa*, a beautiful and singular looking species of the tribe, commonly called the traveller's friend from water always being found lodged between the foot stalks of the leaves, and the stem; also the india rubber tree; (*Ficus elastica*) and numerous other curious and rare trees and plants only to be found growing in their beautiful natural luxuriance under a vertical sun. Besides these many of the more northern productions of India; from the region at the foot of the Himalaya mountains, and from the Nepaul country, have been transplanted and naturalized here, under the skilful and judicious management of the learned professor who superintends these arrangements.[1]

At this time, the Superintendent was a Dane, Nathaniel Wallich (1786–1854), who had joined as Superintendent in 1817, holding the post until 1846. The garden was known as 'Wallich's pet' and during the twenties it was the great pleasure ground of Calcutta. Under his aegis Roxburgh's scheme for

[1] R. Smith, *op. cit.*, 31–3.

adding to the systematic knowledge of India's flora was continued.[1] The Company's team of Indian artists continued to paint new specimens and these drawings were added to the Herbarium's collection. Some were used by Wallich for the engravings in his *Tentamen Florae Nepalensis Illustratae* (1824–1826) and his *Plantae Asiaticae Rariores* (1830), and in the preface to the latter book he notes that 'the present work consists of a selection of plants made chiefly from a series of 1200 drawings, executed under my direction by Indian artists, at the Calcutta Gardens, and on my various journeys'. This tradition of painting by a team of mainly Indian artists continued throughout the nineteenth century, and in 1895, when J. D. Hooker wrote his book on Orchids, there were about seven thousand paintings in the Calcutta Herbarium, almost all of which were Indian work.

Dr John Forbes Royle

If the Sibpur Garden was the most important of the botanic gardens established by the Company, a second at Saharanpur in the United Provinces fulfilled a similar, if more modest function. The Saharanpur Garden had been started by the Mughals in the mid-eighteenth century, but after falling into decay, was taken over by the Company in 1818 for the culture of medicinal plants. Here under John Forbes Royle (1799–1858) plants were listed and drawings made in the same way as at the Sibpur Garden.

Royle, a surgeon in the Company's employment, had spent his early years from 1819 to 1823 in various parts of Bengal and had become particularly interested in the medicinal properties of plants and their geographical distribution. His appointment to Saharanpur with its two hospitals and Botanic Garden was an appropriate one. While posted in this station he was able to study the flora of the Himalayas in the area between Saharanpur in the south and Kashmir in the north. Royle described these expeditions through the mountains in his journal, and his descriptions betray the excitement with which he traversed this unexplored area.

In ascending the Choor mountain on the 9th of May, at first the ordinary Himalayan

---

[1] Wallich was a Dane who had originally gone to the Danish settlement of Serampore as a doctor in 1807 and had there met the missionary and botanist, William Carey. When the settlement was taken over by the East India Company in 1813, he joined the Company's service. He was temporarily in charge of the Calcutta Botanical Garden from 1815 to 1816.

trees, such as *Rhododendron arboreum* and *Quercus lanata*, were met with; the pines then made their appearance. Everything looked like the revival of spring, some of the trees were putting forth new leaves, others, as *Viburnum*, *Acer*, and *Ribes*, were in flower. The ground was covered with a profusion of beautiful flowers, among which *Primula denticulata* and *petiolaris*, *Potentilla atrosanguinea* and *splendens*, with species of *Trillium*, *Anemone*, *Ranunculus*. . . . Higher up, patches of snow were seen, and the Himalayan bamboo, which had been levelled to the ground. Beyond this everything had a wintry aspect; the snow lay in masses though detached, having melted away from around the trunks of many trees and the blocks of gneiss rocks. Few plants were even in leaf, but the Yew was in flower, and the Juniper seen straggling over the rocks, and *Primulas* peeping up in the warmer situations.[1]

Although Jacquemont and Dr Govan had preceded him in the Himalayas, Royle, on expeditions of this type, made some of the earliest collections in the Himalayan area, and they were later arranged at his herbarium.

Like the Calcutta botanists, he also employed Indian artists to paint his specimens, and these drawings were kept along with the dried plants. Although one draughtsman in particular seems to have been very competent, Royle cannot have been wholly satisfied with the work of his painters, for when Wallich was on leave in 1828, he borrowed, with Lord Amherst's consent, the Calcutta Herbarium's team of Indian painters. They moved to Saharanpur and while there made a number of drawings, some of which, together with others by his own artists, were embodied in his *Illustrations of the Botany and other Branches of the Natural History of the Himalayan Mountains and of the Flora of Cashmere*. This beautifully illustrated book was published in eleven parts between 1833 and 1840.

After his retirement in 1831 Royle published a number of learned papers on Indian Botany and Medicine. He was Professor of Materia Medica and Therapeutics at King's College, London, from 1837 to 1856. He continued to be closely associated with Indian matters and was in charge of the Hall of Indian Products both at the Great Exhibition of 1851 and also at the Paris Exhibition of 1855. He assisted Wallich in listing the dried plants in the East India Company's Museum, and Wallich in his catalogue recorded that, 'I have been enabled to add the following two indexes through the generous and valuable assistance I have received from my highly esteemed friend Mr

[1] H. Stansfield, 'The Royle Herbarium', *The North Western Naturalist*, June 1953, 263–4.

Royle, late Superintendent of the Botanical Garden at Saharanpur. This indefatigable and admirable botanist has lately arrived in this country from India with a magnificent collection of dried plants.'[1]

On retiring from India, Royle had brought home a complete set of dried specimens from Saharanpur together with drawings. A second set of specimens remained in Saharanpur and a third set was sent to the Company's Museum. At his death, Royle's own collection was divided and his private herbarium, together with a number of plant drawings, was sold to the Liverpool Chemists' Association by his wife and has now passed to the Liverpool City Museum. A number of the original drawings for the botanical plates in his book are in this collection.[2] His zoological drawings, however, were given to the India Office Library. This collection of thirty-five drawings (NHD 5, Nos. 770–804) consists of twenty-three drawings of birds, mammals and reptiles and twelve of insects. The former were painted by Royle's Indian artists and the latter by John Obadiah Westwood from Royle's own specimens. Westwood (1805–1893) was a famous Victorian entomologist, who in addition to being Hope Professor at Oxford, was also an accomplished artist. The originals of portions of five plates in Royle's book are amongst these drawings in the India Office Library.

Dr Benjamin Heyne

Besides Superintendents of Gardens, official botanists also commissioned artists, and in the south Dr Benjamin Heyne made a large collection of drawings between about 1780 and 1819. Arriving in India in 1777 as a Moravian missionary at Tranquebar, he later entered the East India Company's service. From 1793 to 1819 he was the Company's Botanist in the Carnatic and was also Superintendent of the Pepper and Cinnamon Plantations in Madras. On various occasions he was attached to the Company's surveys as surgeon and naturalist, and for a time he served Colonel Colin MacKenzie in that capacity on the famous Mysore survey. Lord Valentia met him at Bangalore in 1804 during his period of office (1802–1808) as Superintendent of the Gardens there.

[1] MSS. Eur. G. 32, No. 393 of Kaye's *Catalogue of Eur. MSS.*
[2] H. Stansfield, 'Plant collecting in the Himalayas', *Liverpool Bulletin*, III, No. 3, March 1954.

Mr Heyne, the Surgeon at this station [he wrote], waited upon me. I found that he had expected me, and provided for my accommodations in the palace of Hyder within the town, where there are very handsome gardens in the Asiatic style. He presented me with the seeds of several plants, and drawings of them, possessing great merit, by a native. His knowledge of botany, and his indefatigable exertions will render the collection he is forming of the plants of the table-land of Mysore, valuable and interesting.[1]

Heyne was a keen botanist from the moment he reached India and in his early years was a member of the 'Madras Brethren'. The 'Brethren' were a group of friends, which included Roxburgh, Koenig, Rottler, Klein, Anderson and Berry, all of whom had active botanical interests, corresponded regularly with each other and met periodically to exchange information. They took a witty delight in adding the abbreviation '*Nob*' after the names of new types discovered by them. A botanist when publishing a new name can indicate that it is new by adding *nobis* (abbreviated to *nob*) after the name of the plant, and the 'Madras Brethren' enjoyed using the word in its literal and plural meaning.[2]

During his years as Company's botanist on the Madras Establishment, Heyne, like his predecessors Russell and Roxburgh, employed Indian draughtsmen, and thus built up a large collection of flower paintings. In one of his journals he describes how he was able to collect drawings while out on tour. In July 1798, he wrote, 'As Plants were daily brought in, I ordered the Painter to draw only the outlines with Indian Ink, and colour only one flower, fruit, and leaf; by doing which I get a great many more plants drawn.'[3] On returning to his headquarters, he would then have them fully coloured.

Many of these drawings passed to the second Lord Clive, who, as we have already seen, was Governor of Madras from 1798 to 1803. Heyne appears to have been well acquainted with him, and the Library's Day Books record a visit of Heyne and Lady Powis to the Library while he was on leave in 1812 to 1814. The India Office Library unfortunately possesses none of the botanical drawings but it has thirty-four drawings of birds (NHD 1, Nos. 32–75, Plate 14) which belonged to him and which he presented to the Library on 18th October 1813, while on leave.

[1] G. Annesley, *Voyages and Travels to India*, etc. (London, 1809), i, 356.
[2] R. Wight and G. A. Walker-Arnott, *Prodromus Florae Penins. Ind. Or.* (London, 1834), i, xi.
[3] R. H. Phillimore, *Historical Records of the Survey of India* (Dehra Dun, 1945–54), ii, 405.

Dr Francis Buchanan and William Lloyd Gibbons

The second step taken by the Company towards the encouragement of research into natural history was the establishment of an 'Institution for Promoting the Natural History of India' with a menagerie and aviary at Barrackpore. A great impetus was given to this work by the Marquis Wellesley, while Governor General. As we have already seen, he was himself keenly interested in natural history and his attitude to the Company's responsibility in this field was broader and far less commercial than that of the Company's Directors. On 26th July 1804 he issued a Minute on Natural History in which he pointed out that

the knowledge hitherto obtained in Europe respecting certain branches of the natural history of the continent of India and of the Indian isles is defective. Notwithstanding the progress which has been made within the last twenty years in the prosecution of scientific enquiries connected with the manners, produce, and antiquities of this part of Asia, many of the most common quadrupeds and birds of this country are either altogether unknown to the naturalists of Europe, or have been imperfectly and inaccurately described.

The illustration and improvement of that important branch of the natural history of India, which embraces an object so extensive as the description of the principal parts of the animal kingdom, is worthy of the munificence and liberality of the English East India Company, and must necessarily prove an acceptable service to the world.

To facilitate and promote all enquiries which may be calculated to enlarge the boundaries of general science, is a duty imposed on the British Government in India by its present exalted situation, and the discharge of that duty is in a more especial manner required from us, when any material addition can be made to the public stock of useful knowledge without involving considerable expense.[1]

As early as 1800 the Marquis Wellesley had ordered the collection of birds and quadrupeds at Garden Reach for his proposed Fort William College. When the Directors, who did not share his intellectual curiosity, vetoed this scheme, he endeavoured to achieve a similar end through the Institution for Promoting the Natural History of India. This was established in 1804 at Barrackpore with a menagerie and aviary and came to be popularly known as

[1] R. M. Martin, *Despatches* (London, 1836–40), iv, 674.

'The Barrackpore Menagerie' (Plate 23). The institution was placed under the supervision of Francis Buchanan (1762–1829), who had been attached to the Governor-General's staff as Surgeon since 1803. This Company Surgeon had already proved himself an outstanding naturalist and he was eminently suited to such a venture. He was entrusted with establishing the institution and directed 'to collect materials for a correct account of all the most remarkable quadrupeds and birds in the provinces subject to the British Government in India'. Civil and military officers all over India and the East Indies received circulars enjoining them to send specimens to Barrackpore, 'where the quadrupeds and birds which may be collected for Dr Buchanan will be kept until they shall have been described and drawn with that degree of attention to minute distinctions, which is essentially necessary for the purposes of the natural historian'. The accounts reveal that Rs 500 were to be spent each year on the upkeep of the birds and animals, Rs 300 on their collection, Rs 100 on the artist and Rs 60 on paints, brushes and stationery. Buchanan's 'observations . . . together with the drawings of each subject', were to be 'transmitted once in each season to the honourable the Court of Directors, with a request to the honourable Court to direct the publication of the work, in such manner as they may deem most proper'.[1]

As with so many of Wellesley's schemes, the Company's Directors unfortunately did not give this venture a chance to flourish. In 1805 the Governor-General was recalled and Buchanan after little more than a year at Barrackpore went on leave and was then sent to the districts on survey work. Through voluntary help research continued at Barrackpore for another three years, until 1808, and during that time a large number of drawings of birds, mammals and reptiles were despatched to the Company together with lists and descriptions. These lists (MSS.Eur.D.94 and 541) show that many enthusiastic officers had responded to Wellesley's circular, and specimens had been received at Barrackpore from much of India and the East Indies: from a Mr Ure, Surgeon at Hyderabad, a Mr Gibb at Pusa, a Mr Moore, Surgeon of Monghyr, Mr Colebrooke from Benares and Berar 'where he was Resident', a Mr Farquhar, Governor of Pulo Penang, a Mr Cooke, Surgeon of Sylhet and Mr Loftie, Surgeon in the Garrison in Malacca. Presents received by the

[1] R. M. Martin, *ibid.*, iv, 675.

Marquis Wellesley were passed on to the menagerie and aviary. The catalogue records, for example, that Australian specimens were presented to him by Captain Kent of the *Buffalo*, a sloop of war which arrived in Calcutta from New South Wales. A parrot bears the note, 'A very beautiful specimen of this bird is now in the aviary. It was presented to Marquis Wellesley by Captain Kent of the *Buffalo*.' In spite of this activity, the Directors took no action and while Calcutta residents and their children continued to visit the Barrackpore Park and wonder at the strange birds and animals contained in its cages, the magnificent drawings and careful descriptions were allowed to lie in the Company's Museum disregarded.

It is this circumstance which explains the bewildering confusion in which until recently this great collection (NHD 2, Nos. 186–284 and NHD 3, Nos. 311–536) has languished. Buchanan appears to have taken some of the drawings home with him when he went on leave and these he presented to the Company in 1806. While on leave, he was succeeded as Superintendent by William Lloyd Gibbons, an assistant at the Calcutta Orphan School and a member of the Bengal Asiatic Society. It had not been easy to find a successor as the post was honorary. Buchanan had succeeded in combining the work there with his post of Surgeon to the Governor-General's staff. But future Governor-Generals did not share Wellesley's enthusiasm for natural history and no surgeon was appointed to succeed him. Buchanan was aware of the difficulty and in a letter of August 1805 he suggested Gibbons as his successor.

As no emolument is attached to the office of Superintendent, it may perhaps be difficult to procure a person qualified and willing to take charge of my office; and should a difficulty really happen, I most humbly beg to recommend Mr Gibbons, assistant teacher at the orphan school, as a gentleman who is perfectly well acquainted with everything that has been done by the institution, while under my charge, and who is well qualified to give an account of the animals of India.

Gibbons must have been another of those keen amateur natural historians in Calcutta for he agreed to carry on the work. From August 1805 until April 1807 he acted as Superintendent of the Barrackpore Institution and the work begun by Buchanan was continued. Drawings were made and careful descriptions written. Twice during this period Gibbons despatched drawings to London. In a letter of 26th January 1807 (MSS. Eur. D. 562/21, f. 6) he wrote:

I have the Honor to send for transmission to the Honble Court of Directors, a Box containing 50 Drawings of Birds, which have been made since I took charge of the institution for promoting the Natural History of India.

The Descriptions which accompany them, are not so complete as I could wish, this is partly owing to my confined situation, and to the difficulty of procuring from the Natives of India, any information on the subject of Natural History.

The Drawings were from living subjects, mostly procured in the neighbourhood of Calcutta.

A few of the descriptions were made by Dr Buchanan before he left India, and some new names were invented by him, these are distinguished by the letter B. at the end.

A few of the Birds may prove to be new species, I have not, however, given trivial names to them, as that can best be done by the naturalists in England, who have opportunities of being acquainted with all the species of each genus, I wish likewise to avoid changing names which might be necessary on account of new publications on zoology, some of which I understand are now in the press.

There are also in the same box, five drawings which were made by the directions of Dr Buchanan but not copied before his departure. These are marked with a B. in red ink.

These fifty bird drawings are presumably incorporated in the 'G & B' (Gibbons and Buchanan) Collection (NHD 2, Nos. 186–284, Plate 4) and the five drawings with a red B are there also (Nos. 280–4).

On 27th June 1807 Gibbons despatched a further consignment of drawings and descriptions:

I do myself the honour of sending the Drawings which have been made during the time that the Institution for promoting the Natural History of India was under the charge of my predecessor Dr Francis Buchanan and myself. They are in number 230 and contained in four Port-folios. There are also two other Port-folios containing unfinished drawings etc. The Descriptions, etc., accompanying them.

Some of these drawings were apparently combined with the earlier despatch to form the ninety-nine drawings which are now in the 'G & B' collection. The remainder were probably combined with those which Buchanan had presented in 1806 to form the 'Buchanan Collection' (NHD 3, Nos. 311–536, Plates 9, 10, 18, 19). One picture bears the date 'Recd Jan. 1808'.

Gibbons relinquished the post of Superintendent in April 1807 and either went on leave or died (he is referred to in one of the Library's lists as 'the late Mr Gibbons'). Some of his drawings were apparently left with Dr Fleming (see page 23) for when Buchanan returned from leave he visited Barrackpore and went through Gibbons' papers in order to find the descriptions of the drawings left by him. On 29th January 1808 he sent these to Fleming. 'I send you by the bearer all the Descriptions that I have been able to collect from the papers of Mr Gibbons relative to the drawings made under his inspection and which were left with you, together with such additions as I have been able to make from my own observations. You will observe that the descriptions were written in my own name, but I have not failed to notice wherever I have borrowed from Mr G's authority.'

These drawings were duly sent home to the Company's Library in January 1808 and were received in August, being added to the Buchanan collection. The descriptions sent at various times were then bound together in two volumes and combine the notes made by Buchanan and Gibbons.[1]

Duplicates of all these drawings were presumably kept at Barrackpore, but some originals appear to have remained there also. When the Governor-General, the Earl of Moira, instructed Buchanan in 1815 to leave all the natural history and survey drawings in India, a number of zoological drawings from Barrackpore were handed over to Wallich for copying at the Botanic Garden. A few years later, in December 1816 and July 1818, some of these original drawings, together with some of Buchanan's botanical paintings, were sent to the Court of Directors by Wallich. The remainder, many of them copies, were seen by McClelland at the Botanical Garden in 1836 and it is probably these which eventually found their way to the Library of the Asiatic Society of Bengal in 1842 and 1843. A number, however, are untraced, and from what was once a vast and comprehensive collection, only two hundred and twenty-six Buchanan drawings and ninety-nine 'G & B' drawings remain in the Library.

---

1 See S. L. Hora. 'On the Manuscript Drawings of Fish in the Library of the Asiatic Society of Bengal. II. Fish Drawings in Buchanan-Hamilton's Zoological Drawings.' *Journal and Proceedings of the Asiatic Society of Bengal*, XXII, 1926, No. 3, 99–115, and also 'Lists of Drawings: Birds and Quadrupeds'. India Office Library. MSS. Eur. D. 562/21.

Eudelin de Jonville

Besides founding menageries and botanical gardens, the Company also financed expeditions and surveys, and these, although usually planned for some particular administrative, political or commercial purpose, indirectly added to the knowledge of natural history in the East. The surveys were found essential as a basis for efficient administration both in India and in the Company's possessions in the eastern archipelago—Sumatra, Penang and Java; and, as the Company's influence extended, expeditions were also made to border countries such as Nepal, Burma and Afghanistan as well as to the little known Siam, Cochin China and even China itself. With all these regions the Company had hopes of future trade relations and it was by some of the Company's most brilliant servants that these expeditions and surveys were conducted.

After capturing Ceylon from the Dutch in 1796, the Company began to encourage research into its natural history, especially into cinnamon, the main export of the island. The first systematic work was undertaken by Eudelin de Jonville who was directed to survey the cinnamon plantations. This mysterious Frenchman emerges from the shadows in 1798, spends seven vigorous years in the island, and then again disappears into obscurity.

He appears to have been a protégé of Frederick North, the first Governor of Ceylon from 1798 to 1805. On being appointed, North expressed his desire to 'carry out two or three Young Persons from this Country, with a view of employing [them] in extra Services on the Island, such as the interpretation of Languages, the investigation of the natural productions of the Island, with a view to its future Cultivation and improvement, and likewise intending them to assist the Servants on the regular Establishment, in writing Letters, copying Papers, and such other business as might not fall under any specific description.'[1] One of these 'young persons' was de Jonville and on reaching Ceylon he was set to study the cultivation of cinnamon and with the help of the military to survey the cinnamon gardens. By October 1799 North told the Court of Directors that the work was progressing well.

Mr Ionville Superintendant of the Cinnamon Gardens under Mr Greenhill, has for

[1] Letter from Dundas to the Chairman, 1st May 1798. Ceylon Records, 53.

some time been engaged in Surveying of these valuable Plantations, but as this is a tedious & excessivelly laborious service, & altho considerably advanced is by no means finished; I will defer forwarding to you that Gentlemans Reports untill I can present them in a more complete & arranged form. In the present stage of the business however, I am happy to inform your Honble Court that from his exertions I entertain the most sanguine hopes of being able to reduce considerably the expences of the Cinnamon Department and to ensure to you a regular & ample supply of that valuable Spice.[1]

On 19th October 1799 North was able 'to transmit a paper, drawn up', he says, 'in my opinion, with great accuracy and discernment, by Mr Jonville'.[2] At the same time a committee was appointed 'to enquire into the Titles of persons having possessions in the Cinnamon Gardens & for Settling for them a suitable exchange'. De Jonville was one of its members.

Despite this great activity, however, de Jonville was obviously disappointed. He had had to concentrate to such an extent on the cultivation of cinnamon that he had not found time to investigate a wider sphere of natural history. And his disappointment is made clear in a letter of North's written on 30th January 1800.

The constant occupation of Mr Jonville in the more important Concerns of the Cinnamon Gardens, has hitherto not enabled that Gentleman to employ his zeal and Knowledge so effectively as He could have wished in those Researches. A Letter from Him, which I subjoin ... will however inform Your Honourable Court of what has been acquired by Him, & what may shortly be expected towards the general Increase of Physical Knowledge, and the peculiar Enrichment of your museum.[3]

De Jonville wrote:

Your Excellency has been pleased to request I would inquire into, and Collect, whatever regards the Natural philosophy, the natural history, and the meteorology of this Island, Likewise that I should inform myself, concerning the Customs, usages, history, and even the languages of the Country. You have also Directed me to study the Cultivation of the Cinnamon tree and to oversee the Gardens where it is found, and to consider this as my principal occupation and Duty. I have done so, circumscribed however as I have hitherto been, by the greater importance of the gardens which surround Colombo, and which occupy a space of 80, or 100 square miles, I have not yet been able to Extend

[1] Governor North to the Court of Directors, 5th October 1799. Ceylon Records, 52.
[2] Ceylon Records, 11.
[3] Governor North to the Court of Directors, 30th January 1800. Ceylon Records, 52.

my researches to those situated in the interior, and at the Extremities of the Island. In visiting the latter, I should have acquired the means of better fulfilling the first part of your Commands, I would have met with a greater variety of productions of the Island, and have attained a more Extensive information of what regards the manners of the inhabitants, and of the variations which Different Situations occasion in the climate, I have notwithstanding made a Considerable Collection of Natural Curiosities; but have not been able as yet to arrange them. It is only at this moment, when an opportunity of transmitting them to England has presented itself, that I learn the h^ble Court of Directors intention of forming a Cabinet of all the curious productions of india. It is extremely painful to me, my not being at present able to testify my desire of Contributing to this grand project. I Dare not even risk sending what I have already Collected, many objects requiring an accompanying Description which could be made on the Spot only where they are Collected That of plants, for Example, in *hortus-Siecus* [*sic*], must from the destruction of the small parts Composing their flowers, and from the fading of their Colours be always attended with error. Among insects, again, there are a great number that with life, loose also the Scales which adorned them; and in which the characteristick Details of their Genus, are so Effaced as to leave the Naturalist in total uncertitude or lead him into error. The same takes place with Respect to reptiles and fish. All ought to be accompanied with a description Explaining what they were in a Cadaverous, as well as animated state.

Not but that I have actually the Description of about 500 species of all classes, which for want of books, (having only the catalogue of systema natura newly Digested by Gmelin) are still however too incorrect, to authorise my printing them, though under your auspices to the honble Company. Neither have I time immediately to arrange them, in the order required to appear, in a Cabinet destined for the admiration of the world. I may say the same of about 800 Draughts, of which more than half (those of plants) are only sketches in which the details of frentification [*i.e. fructification*] are alone finished: whilst the others, consisting of about 150 sheets shew vacuums only to be filled up with new objects of the same Genus. Your Excellency has often remarked this. I am forced therefore, for the present, to rennounce the pleasure I should have had, in testifying my Eagerness to the honble Company, and in Complying with your wishes in this Respect. I shall be more fortunate the ensuing season, if I am blessed with health.[1]

De Jonville must therefore have been delighted when he was sent with Major-General MacDowall on an expedition to the Court of Kandy in March 1800. He accompanied it as naturalist, draughtsman, interpreter and receiver

[1] Letter from de Jonville, 1st February 1800. Ceylon Records, 4.

of presents, acquiring in the process many facts about the natural history and culture of Ceylon. On return he was appointed Surveyor-General of the Island in a Minute of 16th June, with instructions to institute a new system of survey.[1] There is little doubt that this work enabled him to continue his researches over a wider field. By 1801 some of these researches appear to have been set in order and North doubtless encouraged him to send them to the Company for its newly formed Museum and Library. Governor North forwarded them on 18th February 1801, saying: 'I enclose some memorials from Mr Jonville concerning the natural history of the Island, which will accompany some articles for the enrichment of your Museum. . . . I also send an interesting account by that Gentleman of the Religious opinions of the Worshippers of Budha, which is the Result of his enquiries among the best informed natives both here, and in Candy as per Enclosure (No. 9).'[2] It is these papers and drawings which are now in the Library bound in three volumes entitled 'Quelques Notions sur L'Isle de Ceylan' (MSS. Eur. E 80–2). They were received in the Library on 2nd June 1802.

A little later, on 24th April 1801, an able report on the Pearl Fisheries was forwarded by North, who wrote, 'Great Light has been thrown on the mode of valuing Pearls, by the Researches of Mr Jonville who has discovered the Secret on which the Pearl appraisers conduct their Trade & has delivered it at full Length in his memorial.'[3] This is entitled 'Memorial on the fishing of Pearl Oysters in the Gulph of Manaar'.

With this memorial de Jonville appears to vanish from the Company's records and perhaps future research will show whether he died in Ceylon or returned to England with his patron, Governor North, in July 1805. He must obviously have been a man of varied interests and great talents. In addition to being a botanist and zoologist, he was interested in geology, minerology, ethnology and religion. He acted as Portuguese and French interpreter and was a good amateur artist, not only illustrating his natural history descriptions, but also making sketches of costume and landscape. An engraving in Cordiner's *A Description of Ceylon* depicting the Temple of Buddha at Arandera

[1] Ceylon Records, 5.
[2] Ceylon Records, 52.
[3] Ceylon Records, 6.

near Idalmalpany was made from a drawing by de Jonville.[1] Lord Valentia met him in 1804 and wrote in his Journal,

M. Joinville, a Frenchman, is possessed of considerable talents, and a very great knowledge in several branches of natural history. To his exertions as superintendent of the cinnamon garden, may be attributed the flourishing state of the trade in that article; he has likewise collected the most important information relative to the pearl fishery.

It is strange that so learned a man should remain so nebulous a figure. Even his name is obscure for in the Ceylon records he signs himself both as John and as Joseph de Jonville. Perhaps the British found 'Eudelin' too difficult to pronounce, but when writing a book, de Jonville had recourse to the more aristocratic name. It is unfortunate also that the Company made no effort to publish his manuscript and illustrations, for these would have formed one of the earliest books on Ceylon. Horsfield, however, used them when making his catalogues of birds, animals and insects in the Company's Museum, and Tennant obviously had access to them when writing his *Ceylon*.

Colonel Colin MacKenzie

From 1799 to 1809, Colonel Colin MacKenzie, one of the Company's greatest surveyors and ultimately first Surveyor-General of India, conducted a survey of Mysore. During his early years in India from 1782 to 1799, he had been involved with the Madras engineers in the wars against Tipu, but after the Peace of Seringapatam, when the little-known area of Mysore passed from its ruler, Tipu, to the Company, he was put in charge of its survey, being helped by various doctors, such as Heyne, Leyden and Buchanan.

Amongst the vast numbers of drawings of landscapes, monuments and antiquities made by MacKenzie and his draughtsmen, and now in the Library, are two volumes (NHD 37, 38), one depicting the fauna and the other the flora of South India. The former consists of eighty-three drawings of fishes, birds, animals and reptiles. Most of the fishes were painted at Bellary in 1801. The birds were collected at Bednore, Canara and in the Western Ghats, and were mostly painted in 1805 and 1806. The majority of the animal drawings are

---

[1] J. Cordiner, *A Description of Ceylon* (London, 1807), ii, facing 291.

dated 1805 and 1807, and those of reptiles, 1803, 1805 and 1806. One or two pictures were added after these dates, but the bulk of the collection was made during the Mysore Survey. The fifty drawings of flowers were made at the same time. The pictures in both volumes are carefully inscribed with numbers, names, place and date of origin and measurements, and reflect the neat mind of the engineer. This collection is by no means as systematic or as orderly as MacKenzie's archaeological collections. He appears to have been disappointed in the natural history studies connected with the survey and does not seem to have had a high opinion of Heyne, who helped him during the first years of the operations. 'The *Natural History*', he says, 'was never analyzed in the manner I proposed and expected in concert with the survey.'[1] Nevertheless the collection reflects another facet of MacKenzie's activities. His energy was prodigious and his interests embraced almost every aspect of civilized enquiry.

Dr Francis Buchanan

Similar surveys and expeditions for the Company were made by Francis Buchanan.[2] In 1794 he had been on an expedition to Ava, the Andamans and Pegu. After a few years spent in Chittagong, Tippera and Baruipur in Bengal, he was engaged on the survey of Mysore, Canara and Malabar 1800 to 1801 and in 1802 he was sent to Nepal. So successful were these expeditions, that from 1806 to 1815 he was deputed to survey parts of Bengal, Bihar and the United Provinces. Throughout his career in India, Buchanan retained Indian artists to record the natural history specimens which he collected on his expeditions and survey tours and in this way a very large collection of drawings was gradually amassed illustrating the minerals, flowers, birds, animals, insects and fishes of these areas.

Of these records a volume of pictures of fishes (MSS.Eur.E.72) accompanied by a book of notes (MSS.Eur.E.70) is in the Library. These were the raw material from which Buchanan's *Account of the Fishes found in the River Ganges and its Branches* (Edinburgh, 1822) was compiled, the manuscript of which is also in the Library (MSS.Eur.E.71). This great pioneer work

[1] H. H. Wilson, *The Mackenzie Collection* (Madras, 1882), 6.
[2] For collections of drawings made by Buchanan at Barrackpore, see pages 29-33, 72-6.

embodies the observation of nearly twenty years and includes drawings of fishes made not only at Baruipur but also during the surveys of 1807 to 1814.

Captain William Henry Sykes

The tradition of great surveys created by MacKenzie and Buchanan was carried on by Captain William Henry Sykes of the Bombay Army. During his early years in India from 1804 to 1824 he was engaged in military affairs: he was present at the siege of Bharatpur with Lord Lake in 1805, and from 1817 until 1820 he was in the Deccan commanding native troops at the battles of Kirkee and Poona. All this time he was devoting his leisure to the study of ancient history, antiquities, geology and natural history. As a result he was chosen in 1824 to be Statistical Reporter to the Bombay Government and he was busy with this work until he retired in 1831. During this period he submitted two lengthy statistical reports to the Government, which were illustrated with botanical drawings. He also collected natural history specimens and presented a fine collection of birds to the Company's Museum when he retired in 1831. After leaving India he maintained his interests in the country by becoming a Director of the East India Company in 1840 and its Chairman in 1856. He also preserved his interest in natural history by contributing papers to the transactions of learned societies.

Of Sykes' drawings only nine now remain in the Library, bound up with his 'First Report on Statistics of the Dukhun' submitted in 1826 (MSS.Eur.D. 141). These careful drawings were made for him by his draughtsman, Llewellyn Fidlor, a young Bombardier of the Bombay Artillery, who had been an artist before proceeding to India in 1824. The drawings are now of little importance but illustrate the thoroughness of Sykes' observation.

Dr Nathaniel Wallich

While these extensive surveys were proceeding in India, expeditions were organized to collect information from the little known regions adjoining India to the north and east. Wallich, Superintendent of the Calcutta Botanic Garden, visited Nepal in 1820 to 1821, Singapore and Penang in 1822, and in 1825 toured the foothills of the Himalayas in Oudh up to Hardwar and Dehra Dun. In 1826 he visited Prome, Ava, Rangoon and the Irrawaddy and in 1827 went to Amherst, Moulmein, Martaban, Rangoon and Tenasserim. Several drawings made by the draughtsman who usually accompanied him on these expeditions are in the Library (NHD 5, Nos. 753–64 & NHD 2, 304) including some made in Nepal in 1821 and others during the 1826 and 1827 expeditions to Burma.

Dr John McClelland and Dr William Griffith

One of Wallich's most interesting expeditions was his visit to Assam in 1835 to study the tea plant (*Camellia Sinensis*) and to discover the soil and climate in which it flourished. At this time there was an anxious interest in tea, for the East India Company's monopoly of the tea trade with China was coming to an end. The Board of Directors wished to grow tea in India, and Bentinck, the Governor-General, established a 'Tea Committee' to investigate the possibility. In 1834, Gordon, Secretary of the Committee, was despatched to China for seeds, but in the same year a circular was sent to all East India Company officials asking them for information about the tea plant in India. As a result Captain Charlton reported that he had seen tea growing wild in Assam and he supplied fruiting material. It was then remembered that as early as 1826 David Scott had sent leaves to James Kyd at Calcutta from which he said the Assam villagers made tea. But with only leaves to go by, Wallich had been sceptical and had catalogued them as 'Camellia? Scottiana Wall.' It also appears that the Bruce brothers in Assam had known about the tea plant between 1824 and 1826. As soon, however, as Charlton's specimens had been identified, a Commission was sent to Assam to investigate. It consisted of Wallich, C. A. Bruce, Dr William Griffith and Dr John McClelland. Griffith had entered the Company's medical service in Madras in 1832 and was at Tenasserim when summoned to join the expedition. He had already made a name as a botanist. McClelland had come to Bengal as an Assistant Surgeon in 1830, and soon became well known for his keen interest in natural history, especially geology. He officiated as Superintendent of the Calcutta Garden from 1846 to 1848 and again in 1858. He started the *Calcutta Magazine of Natural History* in 1840 and edited the *Calcutta Journal of Natural History* from 1841 to 1847. He was appointed to the expedition to report on geological aspects.

The story of the expedition is given in Griffith's diary, edited after his death by McClelland and published in 1847 as *Journals of Travels in Assam, Burma, Bootan, Afghanistan and the neighbouring countries.* The diary is illustrated with lithographs made from Griffith's own sketches and gives a clear picture of the country through which the three doctors trudged. Griffith describes the search for the tea plant and its discovery.

Jan. 16th. This day we gave up to the examination of the tea in its native place. It occurs in a deep jungle to the south of the village, and at a distance of about three miles from it. Our route thither lay through first a rather extensive grass jungle, then through a deep jungle. . . . We were fortunate enough to find it both in flower and fruit, owing to its site; its growth is tall and slender, and its crown, at least that of the smaller, very small and ill-developed. Large trees are rare; in fact, they have been all cut down by the Singphos, who are like all other natives excessively improvident. The largest we saw, and which Wallich felled, was, including the crown, 43 feet in length. Small plants are very common, although Bruce had already removed 30,000. Mac. thinks they grow chiefly on the margins of the ravinules or hollows. Their leaves were all large, of a very dark green, and varying from four to eight inches in length.[1]

Griffith later describes how they watched tea being made in the indigenous way.

Here the Singphos demonstrated the mode in which the tea is prepared among them. I must premise, however, that they use none but young leaves. They roasted or rather semi-roasted the leaves in a large iron vessel, which must be quite clean, stirring them up, and rolling them in the hands during the roasting. When duly roasted, they expose them to the sun for three days; some to the dew alternately with the sun. It is then finally packed into bamboo *chungas,* into which it is tightly rammed.[2]

Such discoveries might well have been expected to delight the expedition. Unfortunately, however, personal relations between the members appear to have been far from harmonious. Wallich was ill and irritable. He had failed to take enough drying paper for the expedition and as a result Griffith developed a grudge against him. Griffith was new to North East India and after voraciously collecting plants found himself unable to dry them all. He even caught Wallich removing some of his specimens from the plant presses

[1] W. Griffith, *Journals* (London, 1847), 14–15.
[2] W. Griffith, *ibid.,* 15.

and substituting his own. It is personal friction of this kind which may have underlain the sharp differences of opinion concerning tea cultivation which later developed.

On his return from Assam, Wallich suggested to the Agent to the Governor-General that the tea tracts should be taken over by purchase or lease, fenced in and brought under cultivation. He also suggested that Bruce should be put in charge. Despite his early support for this proposal, however, Wallich later withdrew it. Indeed, by 1839 when McClelland's *Report on the Physical Condition of the Assam Tea Plant* was published, two views were apparent—Wallich advocating areas such as Dehra Dun and Kangra for China tea, and Griffith and McClelland favouring Assam for the indigenous variety. Griffith wrote bitterly,

I cannot conclude without adverting to the desultory manner in which the question of tea cultivation in India has been treated by every author who has written on the subject, with the exception of Mr McClelland. To what conclusion, but one, can we come when we find an authority, who has been supposed to be acquainted with the question in all its details, stating very gravely that a temperature between 30 and 80 is requisite; and when we find that this is as gravely taken up by a popular and more philosophical author.

This attack was obviously aimed at Wallich. In the event McClelland and Griffith were proved right and in 1866 Nassau Lees wrote firmly, 'I have little doubt, that had the reports of Drs. M'Clelland and Griffith received, at the time they were furnished, the attention that experience gained has proved they were deserving of, India instead of *two*, might now ... be exporting annually *ten* million pounds of tea.'[1]

Although there is no drawing in the Library of the tea plant or of any botanical specimens collected during this expedition, there exists a collection of one hundred and eighty-six drawings of birds and animals (NHD 6, Nos. 811–996) formed by McClelland while accompanying Wallich and Griffith. The drawings were illustrations of the specimens which were despatched to the Company's Museum and were presented to the British Museum in 1860. The skins had been roughly preserved and soon decayed. The drawings are therefore of considerable importance and contain at least one type drawing.

[1] G. Watt, *A Dictionary of the Economic Products of India*, vi, part iii (London, 1893), 434.

Following the expedition to Assam, Griffith crossed the unexplored Mishmi Mountains between Sadiya and Ava collecting insects, and then made a second expedition from Assam to Ava travelling down the Irrawaddy to Rangoon. In 1838 he became Surgeon to Major Pemberton's embassy to Bhutan, and the next year, after exploring the Khasi Hills, was deputed to accompany the army of the Indus as it marched on Kandahar. He travelled along the Sutlej to the Indus and Shikarpur, proceeded to Quetta, Kandahar, Kabul and Peshawar, and on the return journey visited Simla, Mussoorie and Jabalpur.

It was on this expedition that twenty-three drawings of fishes (NHD 7, Nos. 1117–39) were made, and a description of the journey is recorded in Griffith's letters and diary. From Kabul he wrote in August 1839:

I am encamped close to Baber's tomb, lulled by the sound of falling water, and cooled with the shade of poplar and sycamore trees, with abundance of delicious fruit, and altogether quite happy for the nonce. . . . I can only find three kinds of fish in this neighbourhood. I have been making some drawings, and collecting a few plants which continue to be entirely European.[1]

His many tours, however, had undermined his health. He was constantly ill and as he brooded on the probable shortness of his life, he wrote from Pushut in January 1840,

My employment is surveying and collecting data for ascertaining the heights of the hills around. But wherever I turn, the question suggests itself, what business have I here collecting plants, with so many in Calcutta demanding attention? How I am living! Alone, without a table, chair, wine, or spirits, with a miserable beard, and in native clothes! But one thus saves much time; how unfortunate that mine now is not worth saving![2]

Later in the year he was ill once more, but by the time he reached Bamean he was again collecting fishes and exulting in their beauty. In August 1840 he noted,

The sun in this country even at elevations of 12,000 feet is very hot, and has excoriated my hands, beautifully white as they were after my sickness, but not before I had caught 3 barbels, evidently different from those of the other side of the range. I caught some trout yesterday evening, it is a most beautiful fish, I was particularly struck with the

[1] W. Griffith, *op. cit.*, xii–xiii.
[2] W. Griffith, *ibid.*, xviii.

size of the eye, its prominence, and expressive pupil, in opposition to the sluggishness of the eyes of carps. . . . Oreinus takes the worm greedily; in the Helmund, 11,000 feet above the sea, it is abundant. It is the same species I think as that in the Cabul river; but in the Cabul river, Barbus is the predominant fish: in the Helmund it is the reverse. How can one account for the small elevation at which fish are found in the Himalayan? I cannot imagine it is owing as some think to the relative impetuosity of the rivers, which after all is only an assumption.[1]

On his way back in Mirzapore in 1841, Griffith mused on the results of this expedition.

To the fish of the various tracts I paid considerable attention, but owing to the difficulties of travelling and of climate, the collection has suffered severely. At Shikarpore I made an extensive collection of the fish of the Indus. I had collected most of the fish of the river, of the Bolan Pass, of the streams of Quettah, and of the Urghundab, near Candahar, unfortunately I relied too much on the preservative powers of alcohol. Subsequently I took the additional precaution of preserving skins separately; and it is to these which amount to about 150 specimens, that the collections are chiefly limited. The collections contain the fish of the Cabul river, between its source near Sir-i-Chushme, and Peshawur, of the Helmund at an altitude of 11,500 feet, of the Bamean river, and of the Chenab, Ravee, and Sutledge.[2]

These specimens were sent to the Company's Museum together with his manuscript report on the 'Productions of Afghanistan' (MSS.Eur.D.159).

After his return from these expeditions he was sent in 1841 to Malacca for a year as Civil Assistant Surgeon. During the next two years he officiated as Superintendent of the Calcutta Garden, where in the interests of science he destroyed the beauty of Wallich's garden by trying to turn it into a 'botanical class-book'. From Calcutta he returned to Malacca where he died in 1845. Like Finlayson (page 48), he was a young surgeon who ruined his health in quest of scientific knowledge. But his researches remain. Although the drawings in the India Office Library are of fishes, Griffith was primarily a botanist and the great ambition of his life was to produce an accurate 'Flora Indica'. His huge collection of plants was eventually given by the Secretary of State for India to Kew and his zoological collection to the British Museum (Natural History) in 1860. The Company, with the help of his friend McClelland, also published his collected papers, and though his

[1] W. Griffith, *ibid.*, xiii–xiv.
[2] W. Griffith, *ibid.*, xxviii.

drawings are of little scientific importance today, they cannot but recall his resolute figure as he sat by Baber's tomb or plodded over the mountains of Bamean in Afghan dress.

Dr Francis Day

Griffith was one of the few naturalists to study fresh-water fishes. The investigation of the fishes of India—rather surprisingly in view of their economic possibilities—lagged behind the study of flora and fauna. Pioneer work had been done by Patrick Russell, who as Company's Botanist in the Carnatic from 1785 to 1789, had collected the material for his *Descriptions and Figures of Two Hundred Fishes collected at Vizagapatam on the Coast of Coromandel* (1803). Buchanan, as we have seen, investigated the fishes of the Ganges during his surveys in Eastern India, and McClelland had also worked on the fish of Bengal. But it was not until the second half of the nineteenth century that the fisheries of India, both fresh-water and salt, were systematically studied by Dr Francis Day (1829–1889). This doctor had entered the Company's service in Madras in 1852 and soon began to study ichthyology and produce papers and reports. In 1864 to 1865 he was on leave in England and wrote up and published the material he had collected while posted in Cochin in 1863. Some of the drawings which he made during this period are in the Library (NHD 8. 1317–24). Numerous other publications followed after his return to India. The six drawings in the Library are a small part of so great a work, but they serve to recall Day's contribution to this economically important branch of Indian natural history.

❦ vi ❦

OFFICIAL NATURAL HISTORIANS AND THEIR COLLECTIONS IN SOUTH EAST ASIA AND THE FAR EAST

Dr Thomas Horsfield

Such surveys and expeditions were made in India or the territories adjoining it. Similar work, however, was proceeding in more remote Company possessions. In Java, under the Lieutenant-Governorship of Raffles (1811–1816), a general survey was started, certain officers being set to investigate the economics of the country and others the administration of the Dutch. Colin MacKenzie, in addition to a land survey and enquiry into land tenure, revenue and trade, recorded antiquities, while Dr Thomas Horsfield (1773–1859) was given facilities for investigating natural history both in Java and Banka. Horsfield was an American doctor who had joined the Dutch East India Company in 1799 and was keenly interested in natural history. In 1811 he was transferred to the British service and soon became an admiring friend of Raffles. The two corresponded frequently, exchanged information and met whenever possible. At their first meeting at Suracarta in 1811, Raffles encouraged Horsfield to devote several months during 1812 to investigating the natural history of the Preanger Regencies. Although Horsfield was primarily a botanist, he extended his researches to cover antiquities as well as fauna and minerals, with the result that a steady stream of specimens and drawings reached the Company's Museum in London. There are lists in the Library (MSS.Eur.D 562/22–8) which record the arrival of all these specimens. When Java was returned to the Dutch after the treaty of Vienna, Raffles and his successor, Fendall, arranged for Horsfield to continue his researches until he retired in 1819. During each of the intervening years, Horsfield, accompanied by a draughtsman and native collectors, undertook an arduous tour to amass specimens and drawings. From November 1812 until June 1813 he toured Banka as a member of the Commission of Enquiry into the island's affairs and resources. A year later he visited the western provinces and in 1815 from May until November toured the eastern districts. In 1816 he concentrated on the lepidopterous insects of Java, but also visited the mountain of Merapi and the south. In 1817 he toured in Mataram and in 1818 in the western extremity of the island. During his last two years in Java he worked hard to complete and order his collections and drawings ready for his retirement in 1819. He then proceeded to the East India Company's Museum in Leadenhall Street as its first Keeper, where he remained until 1859 ordering, examining and cataloguing many of its specimens.

Of these collections of natural history drawings, two by Horsfield are in the Library—one comprising ninety-seven drawings of birds, mammals and reptiles (NHD 1, Nos. 76–172, Plate 5), the other, two hundred and forty-one of Javanese Lepidoptera and mosses (NHD 9, Nos. 1401–1642). With the exception of twenty-five drawings made by William Daniell from Horsfield's specimens in the Indian Museum, all were made in Java between 1811, when Horsfield entered the Company's service, and 1819, when he retired to England. Horsfield records in one of his books the care with which these drawings were made. By 1815 he had trained several draughtsmen in Java for work on botanical drawing, and their skill was soon applied to other branches of natural history, especially the careful drawing of insects.[1] Adjoining his house was a room full of breeding cages containing caterpillars.

As soon as the caterpillars were approaching to perfection a drawing was made of them. The same individual which had been submitted to the draughtsman was then separately confined, watched with the most diligent care, and as soon as it had passed into the state of a chrysalis again made the object of the pencil. A determinate number was carefully attached to the drawing and the cage of the chrysalis. As soon as the perfect insect had appeared and expanded its wings, it was secured, set, and numbered in accordance with the lava and chrysalis. During this period, every possible solicitude was employed to prevent mistakes. The original series, consisting of the perfect insects and the chrysalides obtained by this mode of proceeding, and numbered in accordance with the collection of drawings made at the same time, is now deposited in the Museum of the Honourable East India Company and affords an authentic document of the accuracy of the details regarding the metamorphosis of Javanese Lepidoptera, which will be offered in the course of this work.[2]

These drawings assisted Horsfield in his two main publications on Java and in his famous catalogues of the Museum's mammals, birds and insects.

Dr George Finlayson

Besides making surveys of its territories, the Company periodically sent expeditions to the Far East to investigate trade, and in the course of them further researches were made in natural history. Such an expedition was John Crawfurd's embassy to Siam and Cochin China from November 1821 to December 1822. Dr George Finlayson (1790–1823) accompanied this expedition as Surgeon and Naturalist and in the course of it made a large

[1] The Dutch draughtsmen M. L. Doppert and J. van Stralendorff helped him with some of his insect and plant drawings, but most of the work was done by local artists.

[2] T. Horsfield, *Descriptive Catalogue of the Lepidopterous Insects in the Company's Museum*, part i (London 1829), 7.

collection of specimens and drawings. The journey was described by Crawfurd in his *Journal of an Embassy to the Courts of Siam and Cochin China* (1828) and by Finlayson himself in a journal which was later edited by Raffles as *The Mission to Siam, and Hué, the capital of Cochin China in the years 1821–2, from the Journal of the late George Finlayson, Esq.* (1826).

Finlayson was a young Company Surgeon, who after three years in Ceylon reached Bengal in 1819. He quickly showed himself to be one of the most promising naturalists in India. As he wrote in his journal, 'The *curiosity* that is gratified with inquiring into the laws implanted in organized beings, or into the general phenomena which characterize the material world at large, admits of, and is usually attended by gratification as permanent as it is unmixed; every step is attended with unalloyed pleasure, every new acquisition leads and stimulates to further discovery.'[1] Finlayson certainly found much 'unalloyed pleasure' on this expedition to Siam, which added greatly to scientific knowledge, for this area was as yet unknown to the west. Indeed even today the islands of the Gulf of Siam and the Cambodian Coast have been little visited by naturalists. On the island of Pulo Dinding he writes with excitement about the gigantic epidendrum that Raffles had described.

Nothing in the vegetable world could exceed in beauty the appearance of this stately plant as it stood erect on the stem of an aged tree, surrounded by its flowering leaves, rather resembling the frond of a palm than the leaf of an herbaceous plant. The flowering spike alone exceeded six feet in length, contained nearly one hundred flowers, and was now in full blossom. The flowers exhaled a most grateful but mild odour; they were about two inches and a half across, and upwards of four, including the foot-stalk, in length.[2]

The Sechang Islands were another paradise for the natural historian.

To the botanist these islands afford a most interesting field; and, notwithstanding the numerous visits which we have made to them, much still remains to be done. We never returned from them without considerable numbers of plants that were new to us, amongst which there are some undescribed in our systematic catalogues. . . . The zoology of these islands is scarce less interesting, though more limited, than its vegetation.[3]

[1] G. Finlayson, *Mission to Siam* (London, 1826), xxiv–xxv.
[2] G. Finlayson, *ibid.*, 35–6.
[3] G. Finlayson, *ibid.*, 273.

The Bay of Turong provided many other rare botanical specimens.

To the botanist, the mountains that surround the bay afford a field for researches as interesting, as it is inexhaustible. It would be difficult to specify any locality that produces a greater variety of plants than this. . . . The daily excursions of our party were the means of adding many valuable plants to my collection.[1]

Summing up, Finlayson considered that vast though the field might be, the expedition had undoubtedly achieved something in the scientific sphere.

In speaking of the peninsula of Malacca, I have said, that its unfrequented forests seemed to contain zoological treasures yet unknown to us. A similar remark is no less applicable to the kingdom of Siam generally. There seems every reason to believe that an extensive search would be attended with the happiest results to the science of natural history. Restricted as we were from researches of this nature, we have discovered animals in the classes Mammalia, Aves, and Reptilia, which are either imperfectly, or altogether unknown to the European world.[2]

From this expedition eighty paintings (NHD 5, Nos. 671–751) remain in the Library, illustrating specimens sent home to the Company and later transferred to the British Museum. The specimens were listed in Finlayson's manuscript zoological catalogue, which he made during the expedition and which came to the Library after his death along with his journal and paintings. Finlayson refers to these drawings from time to time in his journal. When describing the excursions to the Sechang Islands he says:

Of birds were procured a fine species of black Pelican, a blue-coloured Heron, several specimens of Columba litoralis, and a variety of the same bird of a bluish cast; another handsome species of Columba, of an iron-brown colour, a green-coloured species of the same bird; a species of Falco of a white colour, and a few others, together with some curious fish, of which, as well as of the former, figures have been taken. . . . Descriptions of these will be found in the catalogues.[3]

Finlayson's journal, in fact, serves as a commentary to the pictures. The white monkeys were sketched at the palace in Bangkok.

They are about the size of a small dog, furnished with a tail about as long as the body. They are thickly covered with fur, which is as white as snow, or that of the whitest

[1] G. Finlayson, *ibid.*, 330–1.
[2] G. Finlayson, *ibid.*, 260–1.
[3] G. Finlayson, *ibid.*, 275.

rabbit. The lips, eye-lids, and feet are distinguished by the inanimate whiteness of the skin noticed in the human albino, while the general appearance of the iris, the eye, and even the countenance, the intolerance of light, the unsettled air they assumed, and the grimace they affected, afforded so many points of resemblance between them and that unhappy variety of our species, as rendered the sight disgusting and humiliating.[1]

And here amongst Finlayson's drawings is the white squirrel which he pursued in the woods on the Sechang Islands and which was later named after him. 'The latter is rare, about eight inches in length; an active, lively, and handsome animal.'[2] Crawfurd also describes it: 'The only quadrupeds which we observed on these islands, were a large species of rat, and a small squirrel about a foot long. This last was numerous in the forest, and we obtained several specimens. It was of a milk-white colour, the paws excepted which were black.'[3]

So strenuous was this expedition that Finlayson overtaxed his strength. He fell ill and died in 1823 on the passage home to England. 'Poor fellow,' wrote Raffles, 'I never had much hope he would be spared; yet his death has been to me a severe shock, admiring and valuing, as I did, his talents, disposition and principles.'[4]

Dr Theodore Edward Cantor

From time to time trade involved the Company in wars—the Opium War of 1840 being one such example. Wars, however, did not preclude the study of natural history, and Dr Theodore Cantor's collection in the Library was a direct result of the Opium War itself.

Cantor (1809–1854) was a Danish natural historian who had entered the uncovenanted medical service in 1835, and from 1837 to 1839 had worked as Surgeon to the Bengal Marine Survey. When he learnt that the Company was about to despatch forces to China, he at once volunteered for the post of Assistant Surgeon to one of the regiments. He then took steps to get himself

[1] G. Finlayson, *ibid.*, 154.
[2] G. Finlayson, *ibid.*, 274.
[3] J. C. Crawfurd, *Journal of an Embassy to the Courts of Siam and Cochin China* (London, 1830), 2nd edition, i, 295.
[4] C. E. Wurtzburg, *op. cit.*, 662.

appointed to collect specimens for the Company's Museum and to research on natural history during his leisure time on the campaign. Cantor describes these steps in his monograph on the zoology of Chusan which he later published.

> In the earlier part of 1840, the Supreme Government had determined upon despatching forces to China. The opportunity this offered of seeing service, and at the same time of visiting a field hitherto closed to science was too tempting to be allowed to pass, and I ventured to solicit the Right Honourable the Governor General to become attached as Assistant Surgeon to one of the Regiments about proceeding on the Eastern Expedition.[1]

His efforts were successful and he was attached to the 49th Regiment. Unfortunately it left India so hastily that Cantor was not able to collect all the materials he needed for his work. He purchased preservatives in Penang and Singapore, but these unhappily proved to be ineffective. He arrived at Chusan, an island south-east of Shanghai, in July and stayed there until March 1841. Fortunately in August 'glasses and spirits of wine' arrived and eased his labours. Cantor's chief problem was leisure, but he trained his servant to collect plants and seeds and he himself divided his time between 'searching for specimens, sketching them and taking notes'. In case his preservatives should all be ineffective, he sketched the living objects with great care and had his drawings copied by Chinese artists. These drawings (NHD 8, Nos. 1151–1292), depicting fishes, mammals, reptilia, amphibia, molluscs, arthropods, plants and agricultural implements, were despatched to the Company along with the specimens and are still in the Library.

Cantor appears to have been particularly interested in microscopic work and his drawings include careful studies of protozoa and cryptogams. He describes how he made these.

> I first took a sketch of the animalcula through single lenses, of which my highest power was $\frac{1}{30}$ single lens, and then examined the object through a compound of 210 linear, when I nearly always found the sketch to correspond. Unless the power of single lenses are added in the sketches, they have been taken through the medium of $\frac{1}{30}$ single lens, and 210 linear compound. The few forms I have added as 'dubia', are such, to which I have found none corresponding among Eherenberg's![2]

[1] T. E. Cantor, *The Zoology of Chusan* (Calcutta, 1842), 28.
[2] T. E. Cantor, *ibid.*, 20.

Microscopic work of this type was unusual in the east at so early a date. Unfortunately Cantor's work was brought to a speedy end. Before long the regiment went sick and leisure time vanished. Cantor worked so devotedly that he himself also fell ill.

The bodily fatigue I had daily to encounter [he wrote], in the execution of my duty, and the distressing nature of the duty itself, I have reason to believe laid the first germs of my subsequent illness. I had scarcely been relieved from military duty, and was busily engaged in turning the short remaining season to the best possible account, when I became a victim to a violent cerebral fever, and was subsequently ordered to sea by the Medical Board at Chusan, in a state, I am informed, which held but slight promise of my recovery.[1]

Despite such desperate conditions, however, Cantor survived and his work in Penang and Malaya remains a vigorous contribution to the knowledge of natural history in the East.

vii

ARTISTS AND NATURAL HISTORY

The collections we have just considered vary greatly in artistic quality and style. Some were made by naturalists themselves and are either unpretentious working drawings or studies suitable for plates illustrating learned papers. Griffith's fishes, for example, are hasty sketches in pen and ink or pencil, tinted with water-colour and surrounded by technical jottings intended to supplement descriptions. Similarly, some unfinished pencil drawings in the MacKenzie Collection were probably rough sketches made by MacKenzie himself for his copyists to redraw. The Sumatra drawings supplied to Marsden by Bell were also the work of an amateur and were useful for the information they conveyed. The drawings of de Jonville and Day on the other hand are clear and competent water-colours eminently suitable for book illustration.

At the same time, professional painters were employed. Occasionally these appear to have been Europeans, but how or why they were in India is unknown. It is probable that a European artist went on Crawfurd's expedition

---

[1] T. E. Cantor, *ibid.*, 31.

53

to Siam and Cochin and made some of the drawings in Finlayson's collection. An artist certainly accompanied this expedition, for Finlayson refers in his journal with disappointment to the visit to Hué as only fifteen people could get into the barges. 'Neither the painter, nor anyone likely to be of much use in procuring objects of natural history was permitted to accompany me.' A certain Edward Reid made many of the drawings for the engravings in Crawfurd's journal illustrating Malay, Siamese and Cochin types, some of which are in the Library's collection of Western Drawings. It seems likely therefore that in Reid we have the painter of Finlayson's specimens. Buchanan's Barrackpore collection contains a few pictures by a certain E. Barton (Plate 19). He may have been a talented amateur from whom Buchanan collected these drawings, but as his name appears in no official list it seems more likely that he was a country-born professional working in Calcutta. The drawings in Sykes' reports were also made by a European painter, Fidlor, a young Bombardier in the Bombay Artillery.

British artists, however, rarely went to India to do such humble work. The majority of the natural history paintings made in India were produced by Indian artists working either privately for British scholars and collectors, or officially for the Company. Under Mughal influence, miniature painting had flourished at many Indian courts. But during the administrative chaos of the eighteenth century, Mughal patronage had weakened, especially on the fringes of the empire, and by the end of the century many artists trained in the Mughal miniature tradition were keen to accept work of any kind, no matter how menial. A few migrated from Hyderabad towards Tanjore and Madras in the south, while others moved from Delhi and Patna to Calcutta in the east. Here were the main British official and trading communities, and it was from these that certain Indian artists sought work.

Private collectors eager to acquire drawings of the flora and fauna of India soon came into contact with these artists and from about 1770 began to employ them for this purpose. In Calcutta, Lady Impey, wife of the Chief Justice of the Supreme Court, engaged at least three painters from 1774 to 1782 to make large pictures of birds, animals, insects and flowers, and Mrs Edward Wheler, the wife of a Member of the Supreme Council of Bengal, who went to India in 1777, also employed a painter. Other collectors did the same, and in this manner small colonies of natural history painters came into existence.

PLATE 2

Squirrels from Sumatra (*Calloscuirus sp.*)
Marsden Collection

PLATE 3

Surgeon and butterfly fishes (*Acanthurus sp.* and *Chaetodon sp.*)
Parry Collection

PLATE 4

Purple heron (*Ardea purpurea*)
Gibbon Collection

PLATE 5

(*top*) Javan porcupine (*Hystrix javanicum*)
(*bottom*) Javan rhinoceros (*Rhinoceros sondaicus*)
Horsfield Collection

PLATE 6

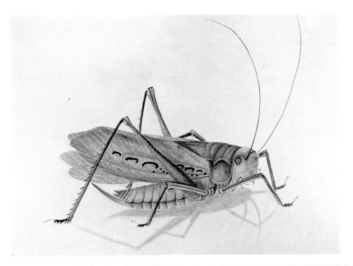

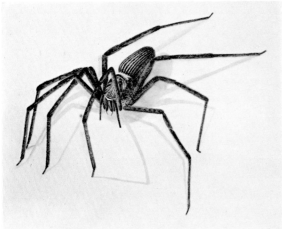

(*top*) Bush cricket; (*centre left*) Banana spider
Chinese Drawings
(*centre right*) Leaf beetle (*Crioceris impressa*); (*bottom*) Scarab beetle (*Catharsius pithecuis*)
Wellesley Collection

PLATE 7

Pied mynah on a Eugenia (*Sturnus contra*)
Wellesley Collection

PLATE 8

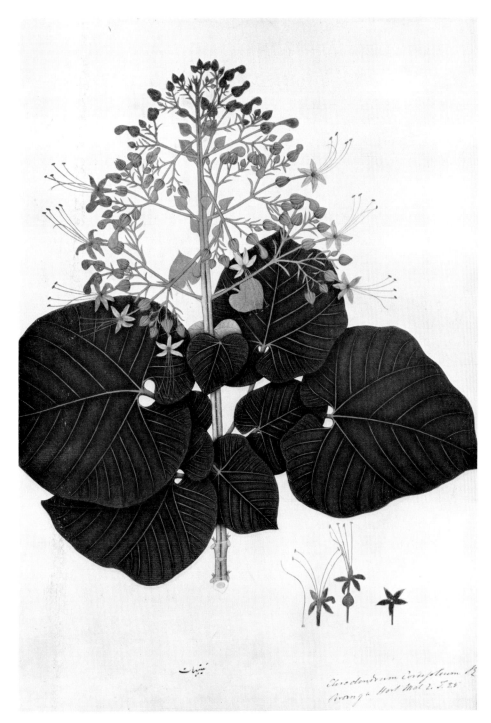

Glory tree (*Clerodendron squamatum*)
Wellesley Collection

PLATE 9

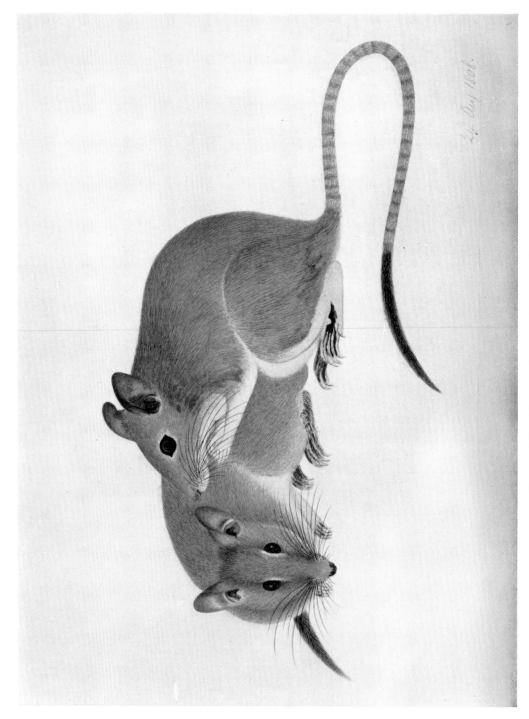

Indian gerbils (*Tatera indica*) Buchanan Collection

PLATE 10

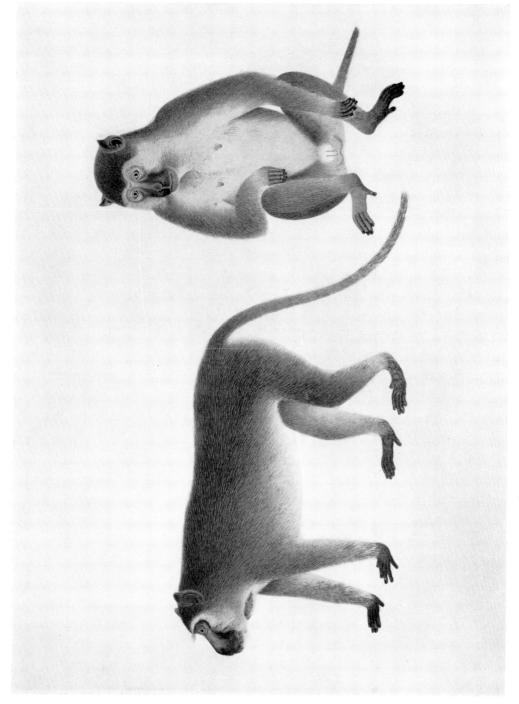

Crab-eating macaques (*Macaca irus*) Buchanan Collection

Plate 11

Castor-oil tree (*Ricinis communis*) Wellesley Collection

PLATE 12

Water melon (*Citrullus vulgaris*) Chinese Drawings

PLATE 13

Mountain ebony (*Bauhinea diphylla*)
Wellesley Collection

PLATE 14

Cuculus orixensis minor

Opisophus melanoleucos Gmel.

Pied crested cuckoo (*Clamator jacobinus*)
Heyne Collection

PLATE 15

Sweet basil (*ocimum americanum*)

Balsam pear (*Momordica charantia*)

Wellesley Collection

PLATE 16

Purple mountain ebony (*Bauhinia purpurea*)

Malabar glory lily (*Gloriosa superba*)

Wellesley Collection

PLATE 17

Peregrine falcon (*Falco peregrinus*)
Raja Serfagee of Tanjore Collection

PLATE 18

(*top*) Mud turtle (*Lissemys punctata punctata*) Clive Collection
(*bottom*) Hog deer (*Hyelaphus porcinus*) Buchanan Collection

PLATE 19

Malabar squirrel (*Ratufa indica*) Buchanan Collection

PLATE 20

Nepal Kaleege pheasants (*Gennaeus leucomelanos*) Wellesley Collection

PLATE 21

Butterfly, praying mantis and aphid on a composite
Chinese Drawings

PLATE 22

Grasshopper and butterfly on a hibiscus
Chinese Drawings

PLATE 23

The Barrackpore Menagerie, c. 1820

PLATE 24

The Botanic Garden House, Calcutta, c. 1820

PLATE 25

East India House, Leadenhall Street, c. 1800

These artists often remained settled in towns but sometimes went on tour with their patrons. Captain Frederick Parr, an officer in the Madras Presidency, employed five Hindu and Muhammadan artists from Trichinopoly for several years and describes the elaborate arrangements for supplying them with specimens.

When the writer's military duties engaged him at the Head Quarters of his Regiment, and as he was desirous to possess as many varieties as possible of the Floral Kingdom, with due attention to quality rather than quantity, he had in numerous instances, samples of Plants brought from other districts into Cantonments, much pains being required to keep them alive during the time necessary for traversing a great distance.

When he went into the countryside, however, his painters went with him.

They were his indefatigable attendants upon nearly all his perambulations. Living under canvas in their company for weeks and months together, exploring in search of novelties the Country Far and Wide, it is but natural to suppose that an enthusiasm would be created only to be understood by those who have in the pursuit of a favourite hobby, ascended wild mountainous tracts, traversed and searched the plains, or penetrated into the deep recesses of the Jungles remote from all cultivation and habitations of men. . . . More than one object was embraced by these delightful and ever memorable Romantic Tours. First the collecting of specimens in Natural History. Secondly the sport afforded to the Rifle, Rod and Gun. And lastly the augmenting the series of Drawings now under notice.[1]

The majority of these artists remain anonymous, but occasionally signatures or inscriptions reveal their identity. Some were Muslims—'Shaykh Zayn-al-Din' worked for Lady Impey and Mirza Sangi Beg for Wellesley. Others were Hindus—Bhawani and Ram Das painted for Lady Impey and Manu Lal for both Wellesley and Richard Parry. All five signed themselves 'artists of Patna', and this would suggest that their ancestors may at some time have worked for Mughal patrons there. Hindi inscriptions on paintings made for Hodgson in Nepal further suggest that painters from Bihar or the United Provinces were employed, since it was in these areas that the Hindi language was most current.

But private collectors were not the sole patrons. The Company itself employed Indian artists as assistants to naturalists on special duty. Both Russell and Roxburgh, when Company Botanists in the Carnatic, refer to Indian

[1] Note in a portfolio of flower drawings sold at Sotheby's, 10th December 1957, Lot 356.

artists who worked for them, and Buchanan mentions the Indian painter who was with him in Mysore. The Company also employed small teams of artists at institutions such as the Calcutta and Saharanpur Gardens, and at the Barrackpore Menagerie. The most expert team was at the Calcutta Garden, and when Maria Graham visited it in 1810 she described how 'Dr Roxburgh obligingly allowed me to see his native assistants at work, drawing some of the most rare of his botanical treasures; they are the most beautiful and correct delineations of flowers I ever saw. Indeed the Hindoos excel in all minute works of this kind.'[1] Paintings made under Roxburgh's supervision were never signed, but from the engravings in Wallich's books it is clear that artists named Vishnu Prasad, Gorachand and 'Rungiah' were at the Botanic Garden a few years later. Artists in Roxburgh's team may also have included Haludar, Mahangu Lal and Gurudayal, for along with Vishnu Prasad their names are written in English at the foot of bird and animal paintings made for the Barrackpore Menagerie in 1804 to 1808 (Plates 4, 9, 10). We know from the Barrackpore accounts that Buchanan had an allotment of Rs 100 a year for an artist. There is no evidence that he employed a group of artists, and the most likely surmise is that they were in fact a part of Roxburgh's team lent by the Calcutta Garden.

Of these Calcutta painters, Vishnu Prasad appears to have been the most competent and the one in greatest demand. The Wallich collection shows that he was the draughtsman whom Wallich took with him on his botanical expeditions to Nepal and Burma. He was lent to Royle at Saharanpur in 1828 and it was largely his drawings that were selected for plates in Royle's *Illustrations of the Botany and other Branches of the Natural History of the Himalayan Mountains and the Flora of Cashmere*.[2] Many of these are lettered 'Vishnupersaud delt'. It also seems probable that Vishnu Prasad contributed to a number of the botanical collections made in Calcutta for amateur natural historians, such as Wellesley and Fleming. Of other artists, little is known except that at Saharanpur a certain Lakshman Singh was deemed the most competent. Royle, however, was apparently dissatisfied with the work of his team or he would not have borrowed the Calcutta Herbarium's artists.

[1] M. Graham, *Journal of a Residence in India* (Edinburgh, 1812), 146.
[2] Many of Royle's drawings are now in the Kew Herbarium. See W. Blunt, *The Art of Botanical Illustration* (London, 1950), Plate 25.

The style of all these artists, whether employed by private collectors or by the Company, was originally Mughal. Natural history had never formed the main subject of Mughal painting, but from time to time various patrons had shown a keen interest in it. The Emperor Jahangir was fascinated by birds, animals and flowers and employed a number of artists to paint unusual specimens. His artist, Mansur, is said to have painted over a hundred pictures of Himalayan flowers during Jahangir's journeys to Kashmir. Animals, birds and flowers, painted with the greatest delicacy, also frequently occur in the elaborate borders of Mughal miniatures. Mughal artists, in fact, could render natural history subjects with great sensitivity. By patiently applying layer upon layer of brilliant body colour and burnishing between each layer, a firm egg-shell-like surface was built up. The finest of brushes was then used and in this way a delicate yet wiry line was drawn across the surface. By this means, the artists could reproduce the lustre of a feather, the roughness of an animal's coat, the velvet texture of a petal, or the tough and leathery surface of a leaf with a delicacy and precision which almost justifies the phrase of Coomaraswamy, 'passionate delineation'.

Such paintings,[1] however, did not suit British natural historians. They considered them too elaborate, decorative and expensive—the delight of the connoisseur rather than raw material for the scientist. The pictures, they felt, took too long to produce, and too much attention was paid to decorative borders and backgrounds. Specimens were not observed with sufficient detail, while accuracy was at times subordinated to the demands of art. What the natural historian needed was a clear and competent drawing which would depict accurately every detail of the specimen and give enlarged details of particular parts of plants or animals. There was no objection to a touch of decoration—a few mossy stones, a patch of grass or the rugged picturesque stump of a tree like those used in British illustrated books—but these must on no account detract from the main purpose of the drawings. The Indian miniature technique provided a competent basis for such work but changes were necessary.

Indian artists were quite prepared to make adjustments and adapt their style and methods. They used European water-colours with the customary

[1] For examples of Mughal natural history drawings see the Johnson Collection and the Dara Shikoh Album, India Office Library.

57

admixture of chinese white, and painted on English paper provided by their employers. They looked carefully at the English illustrated books which were shown to them as models and did their utmost to imitate their general character. They composed the page in a similar manner and added the necessary dissections of flowers and seeds and enlargements of beaks and feet. As might be expected, there is a time-lag in style and many Indian paintings of the early nineteenth century resemble British eighteenth-century engravings rather than the more realistic illustrations of the nineteenth century. Bird drawings are reminiscent of illustrations in Edwards' *A Natural History of Birds* (1743–1751) and Latham's *A General Synopsis of Birds* (1781–1802), flower drawings recall Curtis's *Flora Londiniensis* (1777–1798), while animal drawings are similar to those in Brown's *New Illustrations of Zoologie* (1776). In fact the finest paintings made in India, such as those from the Calcutta Garden or the Clive, Wellesley and Parry collections, recall their British models.

At the same time, it was difficult for Indian artists entirely to change old habits. Unless they were very carefully supervised, some did not always pay close attention to detail and might alter form to suit their feeling for design (see NHD 39). Technique and style also differed to some extent from British drawings. Indian artists did not use water-colour as a wet and flowing medium. They continued to paint with fine brushes, applying the paint thickly so that a shiny surface resulted. Often they burnished the paintings on the back of the paper so that the paint was consolidated and it was then possible to over-paint in order to indicate feathers and fur. Above all, they occasionally allowed personal idiosyncrasies to give their work a strange un-British quality. In bird paintings, for example, the subject may perch on a stump, but the latter is gnarled to an exaggerated degree and covered with lichen-like rugosities (Plate 14). In certain cases, when trees are depicted, they spring from clumps of greenery as in English drawings, but the clumps are dream-like plots with small temples, flag-staffs and bungalows appearing amongst the grass. Wading birds stride through reeds, lush like the plants in Rousseau le Douanier's landscapes. No matter how close the supervision of the natural historian in matters of scientific fact, certain Indian painters felt free to indulge their fancies and produce a type of painting never quite identical with British tastes.

The same adjustments which occurred in India took place in the East Indies. Here private and official collectors both employed local painters—usually Chinese who had migrated there. In China itself, painting for the British similar to that in India had grown up in the Treaty Ports such as Canton and Macao during the late eighteenth century. Chinese painters, like Indians, were extremely adaptable and ready to work for Europeans. Contemporary visitors to China noticed that they could imitate 'with the most exact and servile fidelity'. Moreover 'their fingers were remarkable for suppleness and delicacy of touch'. They were already well known in England from imported embroideries and wall-papers for their realistic rendering of insects, flowers and birds. The Chinese painters soon realized the British interest in these subjects, and as a traveller wrote at the beginning of the nineteenth century, 'The Chinese having found that the representations of natural objects are in more request among foreigners, they pay strict attention to the subject that may be required.'[1]

It was not surprising, therefore, that stock sets of pictures were soon produced for the British depicting flower-gardens, ceremonies, costumes, trades, landscapes, factories and junks as well as sets of fruits, flowers, birds and insects. The latter proved especially popular and were executed on both ordinary paper and velvety rice-paper. The Library has a number of these which reached the Company in the early years of the nineteenth century. Among them are two books of natural history drawings by Chinese artists—one depicting fruits and another flowers, fruits and insects (NHD 42 and 43). Their quality varies greatly, some paintings (NHD 43, i & ii) being standard mass-produced sets for the British market, others, on the other hand (NHD 42 and 43, iii & iv) being strong and delicately executed studies (Plates 6, 12, 21, 22). All, however, from a botanical point of view are over-stylised and inaccurate and do not appear to be the work of artists supervised by a European botanist. It is likely therefore that all were stock compositions for export.

Although these sets did not have any clear scientific purpose or value, it was from the artists who produced them that British natural historians recruited their draughtsmen. As in India large collections were made under British supervision. As early as 1803 the Company had asked its Factory in Canton

---

[1] For these views of the Chinese, see M. Jourdain and R. S. Jenyns, *Chinese Export Art* (London, 1950).

for Chinese pictures of plants and 'miscellaneous subjects'. A letter of 29th January 1804 acknowledges this request, and continues,

The Honble Committee's Instructions respecting the Desiderata for their library has been attended to. A Botanical Painter has been constantly employed in copying the plants, fruits and flowers of this Country, as they come successively in Season and we shall continue him till all that is curious in vegetable nature shall be designed. Mr Ker, His Majesty's Botanical Gardener, directs his employment and sends a description of those already painted which go in the Earl Camden's Packet together with Drawings of the Malacca Fruits by the same Artist.

On 26th February 1806, another letter from Canton notes with pleasure that these drawings have been much admired, and adds, 'We have continued to employ this Artist and he is now engaged under the directions of Mr Ker in completing an additional set of Botanical Drawings as many of which as are ready we propose to transmit to your Honble Court by the present Fleet.' (MSS.Eur.D. 562/16.) These are almost certainly the Chinese drawings that were transferred to Kew in 1879.

Similar drawings were produced for John Reeves, senior, the Company's inspector of tea at Canton. On going to China in 1812, he had been asked by the Horticultural Society to secure pictures of little-known plants in the gardens of temples and merchants, and until he retired in 1831 he sent home a steady stream of paintings illustrating in particular the wonderful peonies, roses, chrysanthemums, azaleas and camellias which he saw in China. He retained a duplicate set which is now in the British Museum (Natural History).

Drawings like these produced under the direct supervision of Reeves and Kew's botanical collector, William Kerr, aroused great interest in England. They gave a clear idea of the beauty of the plants when flowering which could not be judged from the dried specimens or the seeds and potted plants which began to arrive from Canton. One of the main aims of a body like the Horticultural Society was to introduce new ornamental plants into the gardens of English gentlemen and these drawings were crucial in helping experts to decide which flowers would be popular and should be ordered from China. They led to the import of many beautiful flowers which have now become acclimatised in English gardens and greenhouses. Such drawings first drew attention to the Chinese Prime Rose and above all to the wistaria *glycine chinensis*.

The same kind of painting was produced in Malaya, Java and Sumatra where Chinese painters came into contact with British natural historians. Raffles, while at Malacca from 1810 to 1811, employed 'a Chinese Macao painter who was good at painting fruit and flowers to the life'. At Bencoolen from 1818 to 1822 he also employed local artists. Lady Raffles records of her husband that every day after breakfast he

wrote, read, studied natural history, chemistry, and geology, superintended the draughtsmen, of whom he had constantly five or six employed in a verandah, and always had his children with him as he went from one pursuit to another, visiting his beautiful and extensive aviary, as well as the extraordinary collection of animals which were always domesticating in the house.[1]

These artists may well have been Chinese, for Dr Marsden was supplied with drawings from Sumatra by Chinese painters. Several of the plates in his *History of Sumatra* are inscribed 'Sinensis delt' (Plate 2).

Like Indians, Chinese artists adopted British methods for depicting natural history subjects, but at the same time preserved certain Chinese idioms which differentiate their work from both Indian and British. Sometimes the difference between a Chinese drawing and an Indian is slight, but as a rule there is greater softness of texture in a Chinese painting, a more shiny surface and a less wiry line. Instead of curving vigorously across the page, branches meander in more hesitant rhythms. Shading is softer and less abrupt and twigs and branches are touched with silver grey. The butterflies have powdered wings. White flowers are usually given circular blue backgrounds and the sheet is often composed in a more elaborate and decorative manner. In one of the Chinese books in the India Office Library, dragonflies and brilliant butterflies appear hovering over delicately painted sprays of flowers; a medley of grasshoppers, beetles, caterpillars and centipedes is included, while occasionally a lizard or crab is shown scuttling into a corner (Plates 6, 21, 22).

Indian artists do not appear to have migrated to the East Indies in the same way as did Chinese. One of the rare examples is Manu Lal, the 'painter of Azimabad (Patna)', who worked for Richard Parry in Sumatra. It seems probable, however, that he had already worked for Parry in Calcutta and accompanied him to Bencoolen when he was transferred. Few Indian artists

---

[1] S. Raffles, *op. cit.*, 452.

can have had such an adventurous career and few can have met a tattooed 'Poggy Islander'—a careful drawing of whom is in the Library (*Add. Or.* 490) bearing the same inscription as the bird drawings belonging to Parry.

Natural history drawings such as these in the India Office Library are important for several reasons. At their best, they revealed with sensitivity the beauty of the specimen and took their place in the tradition of natural history illustration. They made a contribution to knowledge which, even if superseded by more recent research, was a vital and indispensable stage in the investigation of the natural history of India and South East Asia. But perhaps their greatest value today lies in another direction. In the drawings, executed mainly by Indian artists for British collectors, we possess evidence of that fruitful co-operation in Indian studies which began in the eighteenth century. It is this creative partnership which in last analysis may prove to have been one of the main achievements of the British connexion.

NOTES

NOTE I (page 1)

THE Museum of the East India Company rapidly became so crowded that continual re-allocations of its collections had to be made. In addition to the natural history specimens there were examples of archaeology and ethnography as well as of industrial art. The Herbarium especially was so large that between 1828 and 1849 the Company drastically reduced it. In 1828 Wallich was asked to select one specimen of each plant for the East India Company's Herbarium and to distribute duplicates to other botanical institutions. Before he returned to India in 1832, he arranged for the East India Company's set of eight thousand specimens to be presented to the Linnaean Society.[1] This set remained with the Linnaean Society until 1913 when it was presented to Kew in its original mahogany-faced cabinets. On Wallich's return to England in 1847, he completed the sorting and cataloguing of the material and the distribution of duplicates. He eventually distributed sets to twenty centres of botanical work in eight different countries.

In 1858 when the East India Company was abolished and its property transferred to the Crown, problems of storage again arose. The old East India House was demolished in 1861 and after September 1860 the Library was kept for the time being in Cannon Row and the Museum in Fife House, Whitehall. Further dispersals of the natural history collections were therefore made. In 1859 Kew Herbarium received the Roxburgh drawings as well as 'eleven wagon-loads' of dried plants, and the British Museum was given a great number of mammals, birds, reptiles and insects. The zoological drawings, however, remained in the Library.

In 1869 the new India Office in King Charles Street was ready and it was here that the Museum and Library collections were now deposited. But still the Museum grew until in 1874 the India Office was obliged to lease the Eastern Galleries in Imperial Institute Road, South Kensington, in order to accommodate its over-flowing collections. Once again the Museum moved, this time along with its Keeper, and 'Reporter on the Products of India',

[1] See J. F. Royle's 'Report on the Botanical Collections in India House' (6th February 1849), Home Miscellaneous Series, 787.

J. Forbes Watson. Even this arrangement, however, proved tentative, for after only five years it was decided that the scope of the Museum was too comprehensive. In addition to the natural history specimens there was by this time a collection of over 19,000 objects representing all aspects of Indian life. The contents of the Museum were therefore divided among several institutions. The zoological examples were deposited in the British Museum (Natural History), the botanical in Kew Herbarium, and the geological in the Royal School of Mines. The archaeological and ethnographic objects were sent to the British Museum, while examples of industrial art went to the South Kensington Museum. Of the natural history drawings a number were received by the British Museum (Natural History) and Kew Herbarium, and the rest, listed in the present catalogue, have remained in the Library.

NOTE II (page 1)

The following excerpt from the *Kew Reports* 1879 to 1882 (1880, pages 66–67) lists the drawings transferred to Kew from the India Office in 1879.

As the sequel to the transference to Kew of the economico-botanical collections from the India Museum, the collection of drawings of Indian plants in the India Office Library, 3,359 in number, have been deposited under the direction of the Secretary of State for India in Council in the library of the herbarium of the Royal Garden.

This very extensive collection will be intercalated with the general collection of Icones plantarum at Kew, which is certainly the largest in existence and which it will enormously enrich and extend.

The following is the India Office list of the separate collections of which the whole is the aggregate:

Marsden	48	Royle, Carey and others	1,791
Parry	125	Roxburgh	171
Mysore plants	19	Wight	150
Prince of Wales Island	160	Craufurd (*sic*) and Prince	23
Madras School of Art	4	Finlayson	71
Court	89	Colebrooke	47
Chinese	392	Buchanan	87
Horsfield	59	Hamilton	123
			3,359

In communicating officially the transfer, Mr Stanhope wrote, 'I am directed to add that in transferring these drawings to your custody Viscount Cranbrook is influenced mainly by the desire that a collection so rare and valuable should be made better known and more generally useful to science than it has been hitherto.'

It will be noted that the 'Buchanan' and 'Hamilton' Collections have been wrongly separated and are in fact one and the same Collection. It will also be noted that the Tanjore Collection is called 'Mysore plants', while the drawings labelled 'Royle, Carey and others' have proved to be the Collections of Royle and Wallich.

NOTE III (page 23)

Several sets of drawings apparently made under Roxburgh's supervision are preserved in the Kew Herbarium, but the circumstances in which some of them were made are not entirely clear.

The first and largest group is well documented. It consists of duplicates of drawings made for Roxburgh first at Samalkot and later at Sibpur. These, as we have seen, were regularly sent in batches to the Company together with their descriptions. They are mostly stamped on the back with the seal of the East India Company's Library, and have a printed slip 'Icones Roxburghianae' stuck on the face. They bear numbers and names often inscribed by Roxburgh himself. Most of these drawings were transferred to Kew by the Secretary of State in July 1859, when the East India House was pulled down. One hundred and seventy-one, however, were given to Kew in 1879 after the Indian Museum was abolished. These appear to be some of the drawings which had originally been lent to Sir Joseph Banks, when selecting plates for Roxburgh's *Plants of the Coast of Coromandel* but which had apparently become separated from the main collection.

The second group consists of one hundred and fifty similar drawings presented to Kew by the British Museum (Natural History) in 1889. These have been trimmed so that part of the inscriptions are no longer visible. Certain of these drawings bear Roxburgh's number and some are named and annotated in his hand. Others are annotated in an unidentified hand, and some bear no inscription at all. The origin of these drawings is unknown. It is possible that they belonged to a set kept by Roxburgh for his personal use and broken up at some later date. Some, on the other hand, may be duplicates which Roxburgh left with Carey when he retired from India. (See Kaye's *Catalogue of European MSS.* Note to No. 147.)

A third group consists of two sets of drawings inscribed '1' to '25' and 'No. 1' to 'No. 25', all bearing the same printed 'Icones Roxburghianae' slip which occurs on the first group of drawings. The first sheet of one set is endorsed, '25 Drawings of plants recd from the Secretary's Office, 27th May, 1808'. This inscription shows that this set was also part of the Company's Library and must have been transferred to Kew in 1859 or 1879. These drawings differ from Roxburgh's other drawings in that they have a double-rule frame, and are not inscribed by him. The plant names which they bear connect them with the Madras Brotherhood in South India, and it is therefore possible that these may be some of Roxburgh's earliest drawings which were said to have been 'destroyed by inundation'. If this is so then these drawings must have lain with Roxburgh or one of his friends in South India, such as Heyne, and not been presented to the Company until 1808. Roxburgh was at home on leave in that year and may himself have handed over this early set to the Library.[1]

NOTE IV

There are a few volumes in the Library containing incidental natural history drawings not included in this Catalogue :

1. *The Stringer's Journall*, 1713 (MSS. Eur. D. 5, No. 9 in Kaye's *Catalogue of Eur. MSS.*), containing drawings of a hippopotamus, sea birds and fishes.

2. Peter Mundy's *Itinerarium Mundi*, 1608–1667 (MSS.Eur.G.1, No. 1 in Kaye's *Catalogue of Eur. MSS.*), with drawings of animals, birds, fishes, molluscs, crabs, plants, etc.

[1] I am indebted to Mr J. R. Sealy of the Kew Herbarium for much of this information which he has now included in his article 'The Roxburgh Flora Indica Drawings at Kew', *Kew Bulletin*, No. 2, 1956, and No. 3, 1957. A book of paintings 'Belonging to Dr Heyne', seen by Mr Sealy while this page was in the press, suggests that the third group was made for Heyne.

3. *Drawings of Scenery* made by William Alexander during the progress of the British Embassy to the Court of Pekin in 1792–4 (*Western drawings* Nos. 960, 961), containing about twenty-seven drawings of elephants, a seal, a cassowary, cormorants, penguins, insects, fishes, molluscs, plants and fruits.

4. A set of twelve drawings of birds (*Add. Or.* 801–12) bound in an album together with paintings of trades and servants. Made for the British, Benares *c.* 1835.

CATALOGUE
OF THE DRAWINGS

CATALOGUE

NATURAL history drawings in the India Office Library fall into four main groups.

1. Nine large volumes (NHD 1–9) containing 1578 natural history drawings, probably assembled in 1879 when the India Museum's natural history specimens and many of the Library's drawings were distributed between the Kew Herbarium and the British Museum. They consist of collections received between 1806 and 1866 and were entered in the 1888 Catalogue (Vol. 1, p. 428). The original drawings, if large enough, were bound into these volumes; otherwise they were pasted on to white leaves. Continuous numbers from 1–1642 were inscribed in red ink on the drawings and on certain blank pages in between. Title pages listing the contents were given to each volume. Most subjects had already been identified by Horsfield and Moore when they were compiling the Museum's catalogues of birds, mammals and insects.

2. Two thousand six hundred and sixty folios of drawings bound in 27 volumes (NHD 10–36: 15 vols. of plants and an index volume, 6 of birds, 2 of mammals, 2 of insects, 1 of fishes), originally made for the Marquis Wellesley when Governor-General of Fort William and purchased by the Library in 1866.

3. Bound volumes (the MacKenzie, Buchanan and de Jonville drawings) already catalogued as part of the European Manuscripts Collection. They were clearly retained, when many drawings were given to other institutions, because they formed an integral part of the larger collections made by these scholars.

4. Miscellaneous: some, such as the Clive drawings, have been recently acquired and have been mounted separately. Others, such as those transmitted by Dr Roxburgh, Michael Atkinson, Dr Kerr and Captain Sykes, accompanied papers or reports and have been bound up with these to form part of the European Manuscripts Collection. There remain a few illustrations the provenance of which is unknown.

The present catalogue arranges the drawings alphabetically by collectors.

EDWARD BLYTH
(1810–1873)

(NHD 8. Nos. 1296–1313) Eighteen water-colour drawings of birds from India, Burma, the East Indies and Australia, bound in a volume measuring 21 by 14 inches. (Introduction, pages 12–3.)

These drawings were probably made by Indian artists in Calcutta from specimens sent by Blyth to the Company's Museum while he was Zoological Curator of the Museum of the Asiatic Society of Bengal from 1841 to 1863. The drawings are inscribed with the Latin name of the subject and often with its provenance—the Himalayas, Nepal, Bhutan, Tenasserim, Singapore and Australia. Drawing No. 1302, the *Carpodacus frontalis Blyth*, is probably a type drawing.[1]

Presented to the Library by Blyth in 1863 after he had retired from India (see No. 1302 inscribed, 'Recd from E. Blyth, 1863').

FRANCIS BUCHANAN (later BUCHANAN-HAMILTON)
(1762–1829)

1. (NHD 3. Nos. 311–536: No. 158 in Kaye's *Catalogue of Eur. MSS.*)

Two hundred and twenty-six drawings in water-colour and pencil depicting 169 birds (151 separate drawings and 18 duplicates), 38 mammals and 19 reptilia from India and the East Indies; bound in a volume measuring 21 by 14 inches. (Introduction, pages 29–33, Plates 9, 10, 18, 19.)

The bulk of this Collection was made under the supervision of Buchanan while he was Superintendent of the Institution for Promoting the Natural History of India at Barrackpore between 1804 and 1805. A few drawings, however, which are included in this collection were probably made between 1805 and 1807 when William Lloyd Gibbons, Buchanan's successor, was Superintendent. No. 405, for example, is inscribed, 'Among the drawings of Mr Gibbons left with Dr Fleming. Sent home Jany. 1808'.

The Collection consists of drawings which appear to have arrived at India House at six different times. Unfortunately, at the time of mounting, many drawings were trimmed and the note of their dates of arrival removed. This makes it impossible to group all the drawings by dates of acquisition. There are, however, a number of

[1] The late Sir Norman Kinnear has suggested that a careful examination of the Library's drawings by scientists may reveal further drawings of type specimens now lost.

letters and lists in the Library which record the arrival of certain groups. The number of drawings in the Buchanan and the 'G & B' collection (see page 75) and the number of drawings received by the Library by no means tally and it seems possible that certain drawings were transferred without due record.

The Library's drawings comprise the following groups:

i. Drawings delivered at India House in 1806 when Buchanan was on leave. Although no record of these exists in the Library, zoological drawings in the Library of the Asiatic Society of Bengal bear endorsements, 'Copy of Drawing delivered at India House, 1806'.

ii. Fifty drawings despatched by Gibbons on 26th January 1807 and received on 11th September 1807.

iii. Two hundred and thirty drawings sent by Gibbons on 27th June 1807 and received in January 1808. These two groups of drawings had been made partly under the supervision of Buchanan and partly of Gibbons. Since there are now only 99 drawings in the Gibbons and Buchanan Collection, certain of the drawings despatched by Gibbons must have been incorporated in the Buchanan Collection.

iv. Twenty-eight drawings (26 of birds and 2 of reptilia) sent by Dr Fleming in January 1808 and received in August 1808. These had been left with him when Gibbons relinquished the post of Superintendent in April 1807. The Library's Day Book records, 'Recd from the Examiner's Office, per Castle Eden, 26 Drawings of birds and two of tortoises, transmitted from Bengal by desire of Dr John Fleming for the Library'. No. 405 is inscribed, 'Among the drawings of Mr Gibbons left with Dr Fleming. Sent home Jany. 1808'. An additional consignment, however, must also have been sent at this time for there are 30 drawings in the Buchanan Collection which are inscribed as being received in August 1808, amongst them a number of mammals, which are not mentioned in the above Day Book entry. A list in the Library (MSS. Eur. D. 562/21) records that a group of 26 drawings of mammals was at some time received from Buchanan.

v. One hundred and thirty-five botanical drawings and 14 drawings of mammals and birds were sent by Wallich from the Botanic Garden on 16th December 1816 and received on 21st July 1817. The botanical drawings were transferred to Kew in 1879, but the rest are in the Buchanan Collection and are inscribed '1817' or 'Recd 21 July, 1817'. (Nos. 316, 319, 320, 504.)

vi. One hundred and eight drawings of mammals were sent by Wallich on 3rd July 1818 and were received in the Library on 1st June 1819. 19 drawings in the Buchanan collection are inscribed, 'Recd 1 June, 1819'. In the covering letter Wallich wrote, 'In obedience to the instructions contained in a letter from the Chief Secretary to Government dated the 17th August 1816, I have the honor to send you, for the purpose of their being forwarded to the Honorable Court of Directors 108 sheets of Original drawings of Dr Buchanan, according to the accompanying list, which have been copied since the

16th December 1816, when the first portion of that collection was transmitted to Government.' These apparently are some of the original drawings made at Barrackpore which were left at the Calcutta Botanic Garden when Buchanan retired in 1815. They were copied and then sent to England. The drawings which McClelland saw at the Botanic Garden in 1836 were probably mostly copies, although some originals, e.g. of fishes, still remained and were later sent to the Asiatic Society of Bengal.

Two volumes of descriptions were sent home from Barrackpore. One volume (MSS. Eur. D. 541) is damaged but descriptions of 75 birds remain (Nos. 7–89, 93, 94), while further descriptions of 31 birds, 24 mammals and 4 reptilia are given in MSS. Eur. D. 94. (No. 159 in Kaye's *Catalogue of Eur. MSS.*) Of these latter descriptions, all but three relate to the drawings in the Buchanan Collection. The remaining three apply to Nos. 281–3, the Buchanan drawings in the Gibbons and Buchanan Collection (see page 76).

Many of the drawings are by Haludar (Nos. 481, 482, 484, 487–9, 493, 497, 499, 501, 511, 513, 514, 518–20), who may well have been the retained artist at the menagerie. Other drawings (Nos. 480, 490, 496, 506, 509, 510) were made by a certain E. Barton, who may have been a European draughtsman employed by Buchanan.

A number of the drawings of mammals bear, in addition to the Latin name, inscriptions in Bengali ('of the Bengalese'), in Urdu ('of the Musulmans'), in Hindi ('of Hindustan Proper') and sometimes in Telugu ('of the Telingas'). Inscriptions by Buchanan himself giving the Latin name and provenance occur on some drawings, e.g. 313.

Copies of a number of these Barrackpore drawings appear in the Wellesley Collection, e.g. Nos. 489, 510 and 511 correspond to ff. 13, 19, 25 in the Wellesley Collection of mammals (NHD 33) (see page 97).

Some of the drawings of tortoises and turtles (Nos. 523–5, 527, 528, 530, 532–6) were used for engravings in J. E. Gray and T. Hardwicke, *Illustrations of Indian Zoology* (London, 1830–35).

2. (MSS. Eur. E.72. No. 160.3 in Kaye's *Catalogue of Eur. MSS.*)

One hundred and four ff. of drawings in water-colour and pen and ink depicting Gangetic Fishes, bound in a volume measuring 12 by $10\frac{1}{4}$ inches. 103 fishes are illustrated, one fish (No. 65 and 66) occupying two folios. A coloured side view is usually given with a dorsal view in outline. Sometimes a third illustration or only a coloured side view is given. (Introduction, pages 39–40.)

Some of these pictures were probably made between 1798 and 1800 in Baruipur, Twenty Four Parganas. Others were made during the surveys of 1807–14. A volume of notes accompanies these drawings (MSS. Eur.E.70.No. 160.2 in Kaye's *Catalogue of Eur. MSS.*) and according to them drawings would appear to have been made of specimens at 'Roopgunje, 1807', 'Nathpur, 3rd August 1810', 'Patna, 7th April 1812' etc.

The drawings are inscribed with the Latin name and the Bengali in both roman and Bengali scripts. Notes by Buchanan appear on some drawings, such as f. 88: 'This fin is badly copied. The two last pair of rays should be united so as to form 5 in all.'

The same artist appears to have made all the drawings. Buchanan, while at Baruipur from 1798 to 1800, trained an Indian artist for this work and he may well have worked for Buchanan throughout his career in India.

These drawings were used for making the plates to Buchanan's *An Account of the Fishes found in the River Ganges and its Branches* (Edinburgh, 1822). Ninety-eight drawings were used for 39 plates; ff. 100–104 of the manuscript were not printed.

Buchanan was handicapped in the production of his book by the loss of the survey drawings made between 1807 and 1814 which Lord Moira ordered to be kept in India. These may be the drawings of fishes which McClelland saw at the Botanic Garden, Calcutta, in 1836 and which were transferred to the Library of the Asiatic Society of Bengal in 1842 or 1843. In the manuscript preface to his book (MSS. Eur. E. 71. No. 160.1. in Kaye's *Catalogue of Eur. MSS.*) Buchanan writes, 'I have to regret, that the number of plates is so small owing to my having been deprived of the drawings of 144 fishes. These together with drawings of 20 quadrupeds, of 241 birds and 130 plants the Government of Bengal at the instigation of the Earl of Moira took from me by one of those mean exertions of power, into which a weak man thrust into high authority is liable to fall.'

The Marquis Wellesley appears to have had copies made of many of these drawings. The volume of fish drawings in his Collection (NHD 36) contains several duplicates of Buchanan's illustrations.

This volume of Buchanan's drawings, together with the notes, was received by the Library on 12th November 1823.

FRANCIS BUCHANAN AND WILLIAM LLOYD GIBBONS

('G & B' Collection)

(NHD 2. Nos. 186–284) Ninety-nine drawings in water-colour of birds from India and the East Indies (Introduction, pages 29–33 and Catalogue, pages 72–4, Plate 4).

These drawings, apart from Nos. 280–4, were mostly made at Barrackpore under the supervision of William Lloyd Gibbons while he was Superintendent of the Institution for Promoting the Natural History of India from August 1805 until April 1807, after Buchanan had gone home on leave. No. 261, for example, is inscribed, '1807. Living in the aviary. Said to have a long erect crest'. Five drawings, Nos. 280–4, as Gibbons explained at the time of their despatch, were marked with a red 'B', since they had been prepared for Buchanan before Gibbons took over charge, although the copies for Barrackpore had not then been made. These drawings should by rights be included in the Buchanan Collection. The 'G & B' drawings were despatched in two consignments in January and June 1807.

The 'G & B' collection is clearly a continuation of the work begun by Buchanan. The drawings are inscribed by the same copyist in the same form with Latin, Bengali, Hindi or Urdu inscriptions. The same artist Haludar is still at work and 11 drawings bear his name. All but 8 drawings bear the name of an artist: 37 drawings were made by 'Mahangoo Laul' (Mahangu Lal), 35 by 'Gooroodyal' (Gurudayal) and 8 by 'Bishnoopersaud' (Vishnu Prasad). These same names occur on the zoological drawings in the Library of the Asiatic Society of Bengal. Vishnu Prasad also worked for Wallich at the Botanic Garden and accompanied him on his various expeditions. Certain inscriptions are probably by Gibbons; it may be his writing which occurs on No. 242. Some of the drawings are duplicates of others in the Buchanan collection; Nos. 234, 280 and 284, for example, are duplicates of Nos. 357, 438, 439. Certain of the 'G & B' drawings are also similar to some in the Wellesley Collection. No. 276 is similar to f. 113 of NHD 27 and Nos. 213 and 282 similar to ff. 81 and 95 of NHD 28 in the Wellesley Collection. As Wellesley left India in 1805, this would suggest that these particular drawings in the 'G & B' Collection must have been made in Buchanan's time. It is possible therefore that not only Nos. 280–4 but other drawings also in the 'G & B' collection were made under Buchanan's supervision.

THEODORE EDWARD CANTOR

1809–1854

(NHD 8. Nos. 1151–1292) One hundred and forty-two drawings in water-colour, pen-and-ink, pencil and varnished water-colour depicting 10 fishes, 10 mammals, 8 reptilia, 4 amphibia, 29 molluscs, 1 vermes, 5 arthropods, 7 cryptogams, 2 protozoa, 59 plants, 1 boat and 6 implements from Chusan and Penang; bound in a volume measuring 21 by 14 inches. (Introduction, pages 51–3.)

Five drawings were made in Penang in 1844. Nos. 1155, 1156, 1158 and 1160 were made by Cantor himself, while No. 1157 is a copy from one of his drawings. These are inscribed 'Theo Cantor. April (or September) 1844. Pinang.'

The remaining drawings are all copies of Cantor's Chusan drawings made by Chinese artists between 1840–2. They are inscribed with the Latin name of the subject and 'Chusan. Copied from Dr Cantor's Original. 1841 (or 1842).' The plant drawings bear notes on their habitats by Cantor.

Twelve of these drawings are the originals of the 12 plates in Cantor's *The Zoology of Chusan* (Calcutta, 1842). No. 1159 is the original of Plate 1, No. 1151 of Plate 2, No. 1152 of Plate 3, No. 1153 of Plate 4, No. 1154 of Plate 5, No. 1204 of Plate 6, No. 1205 of Plate 7, No. 1207 of Plate 9, No. 1208 of Plate 10, No. 1209 of Plate 11, No. 1210 of Plate 12 and No. 1211 of Plate 13. Plate 8 is missing and appears never to have been made.

Three consignments of specimens from Cantor were received by the Museum in January, March and April, 1842.

EDWARD CLIVE, FIRST EARL OF POWIS

1754–1839

(NHD 44/1–15) Fifteen water-colour drawings of 3 mammals, 2 birds, 9 fishes and 1 reptilia from the East Indies measuring approx. 14½ by 21 inches. (Introduction, page 8, Plate 18.)

These drawings were almost certainly collected by Lord Clive while he was Governor of Madras from 1798 to 1803 and were probably made by Chinese painters working for the British in Malacca. The illiterate titles on some of the drawings may have been written by the painters themselves, e.g. No. 347, parakeet, inscribed 'Paret'. No. 348, kingfisher, inscribed 'Fishing burd'. No. 349, a *lutianid*, inscribed 'This Malacaw fish. Name E-can-maraw.' No. 354, a *proteracanthus sassifrons*, inscribed 'This Malacaw fish. Name of E-can-mudoo. Upon his head 3 stones.'

These drawings were purchased at Sotheby's in January 1956, from the collection of the Earl of Powis and were part of an album of 19 pictures, 4 of which were purchased by the Indian Section, Victoria and Albert Museum (Nos. I.S. 1–4—1956) and 15 by the India Office Library.

FRANCIS DAY

1829–1889

(NHD 8. Nos. 1317–24) Two photographs and 5 drawings in water-colour and 1 in pen-and-ink depicting fishes from the Malabar Coast of India. (Introduction, page 46.)

The drawings were made by Day in 1863 while he was stationed at Cochin.

The two photographs (Nos. 1317 and 1318) are inscribed, 'Photo by Mr Griggs from original drawing by Dr F. Day'. The remaining drawings are inscribed with the Latin name of the subject and in some cases the vernacular name. They are also inscribed, 'Dr F. Day, 1863. Cochin.'

These drawings were part of the material used by Day for his catalogue of fishes and were brought by him to England in 1864–5. The catalogue was published as 'On the Fishes of Cochin on the Malabar Coast of India.' *Proceedings of the Zoological Society of London*, part i, 18 January 1865; part ii, 14 March 1865. A fuller catalogue, entitled *The Fishes of Malabar*, was published in 1865. No. 1317 is a photograph of the drawing from which Plate I in both publications was made. The other drawings were not used for illustrations.

GEORGE FINLAYSON

1790–1823

(NHD 5. Nos. 671–713 and 715–51) Eighty drawings in water-colour and pencil, 3 of which are unfinished, depicting 43 birds, 14 mammals (including 2 duplicates), 12 fishes, 2 arthropods, 1 echinoderm, 5 reptilia, 1 amphibia and 2 skulls from Siam, Cochin China and the East Indies; bound in a volume measuring 21 by 14 inches. (Introduction, pages 48–51.)

These drawings were collected by Finlayson between November 1821 and December 1822 during John Crawfurd's Mission to Siam and Cochin China, which Finlayson accompanied as surgeon and naturalist. The drawings are illustrations to the Zoological Catalogue (MSS. Eur. D. 136) which accompanied the specimens sent to the Company's Museum in 1823.

Many of the drawings are inscribed, 'Siam, Finlayson', and No. 699 is inscribed 'Sichang Islands'.

A collection of topographical and ethnographical drawings made during this expedition is also in the Library. (*Western drawings* Nos. 972–1000.)

WILLIAM GRIFFITH

1810–1845

(NHD 7. Nos. 1117–39) Twenty-two drawings in pen-and-ink, pencil and water-colour depicting fishes and their organs from India and Afghanistan; bound in a volume measuring 21 inches by 14 inches. (Introduction, pages 41–6.)

These drawings were made by Griffith himself in 1839 and 1840, when he accompanied the army of the Indus to Kandahar and Kabul. They are inscribed sometimes with the provenance and often with rough notes concerning the specimen. They were despatched with the fishes which were received by the Museum in September 1842.

A few drawings were made in the Salt Range and Dehra Dun on his return from Afghanistan; Nos. 1125 and 1128 are inscribed 'Lalpore', and Nos. 1119 and 1127 'Song River. East end of Dehra Doon.' But most of the drawings were made on the North West Frontier and in Afghanistan. Nos. 1120 and 1137 are inscribed 'Peshowur', the latter also 'Nov. 15, 1839'. No. 1126 is inscribed 'Barbus of Bamean river', No. 1122 'Pushut. Feby 3rd, 1840' and, on the reverse, 'Sent to me by Major MacGregor during our visit to Pushut and Olipore. Specimen lost.' No. 1117 is inscribed 'At Basshah—several marches nearer the plains of Toorkistan. Captain Hay says it attains a considerable size' and No. 1135 is inscribed 'Helmund'. Captain William Hay (the son of Mr Hay of Dalhousie Castle near Edinburgh) was Superintendent of the Hill States with his office in Simla.

THOMAS HARDWICKE

1755–1835

(NHD 39) Ninety-six drawings in water-colour depicting 96 birds from Srinagar and Kumaon (U.P.) and Betul (C.P.), bound in a volume measuring 17 by 13¾ inches. (Introduction, pages 8–10.)

These drawings were collected by Thomas Hardwicke during expeditions made to the Kumaon and Garhwal areas in the Himalayas and to Betul in the Central Provinces between 1794 and 1803. A paper describing his travels in Garhwal in 1796 and entitled 'Narrative of a Journey to Sirinagur' was contributed by him to *Asiatick Researches*, VI, 1801.

The paper on which the drawings are made has 1794 and 1801 watermarks. Each folio is inscribed in Urdu giving the name of the bird, its size and weight and the area from which it was collected.

The drawings were purchased from a London dealer in December 1891 and although there is no inscription connecting them with Hardwicke, other evidence (see Introduction, pages 9–10) proves that they were originally part of his collection.

BENJAMIN HEYNE

?–1819

(NHD I. Nos. 32–75) Forty-four drawings in pen-and-ink and water-colour (4 unfinished) depicting Indian birds, bound in a volume measuring 21 by 14 inches. (Introduction, pages 27–8, Plate 14.)

These drawings were collected sometime between 1793 and 1813 in South India by Dr Benjamin Heyne while he was Company's Botanist in the Carnatic.

All would appear to be by the same Indian painter who has a distinctive style. From pencil inscriptions on many of the drawings he may have been named 'Chobi' (Chaubey).

The drawings were given to the Library on 18th October 1813, when Heyne was on leave in England. The Day Book records, 'Dr Heyne presented to the Library 44 Drawings of Indian Birds'.

BRIAN HOUGHTON HODGSON

1800–1894

(NHD 5. Nos. 765–9) Five drawings in water-colour, pencil and oil on thin canvas depicting Indian mammals: bound in a volume measuring 21 inches by 14 inches. (Introduction, pages 11–12.)

The collection was made by Hodgson in Nepal and Darjeeling some time between 1820 and 1858.

From faint pencil inscriptions in Nagari on Nos. 766 and 767, the draughtsmen would appear to be Hindus from Bihar or the United Provinces.

The drawings were apparently sent to the Library together with a memo and specimens. No. 765 is inscribed, 'B. H. Hodgson: unpublished. To be published with description from the present memo & skins & sculls.' Nos. 765 and 767 are inscribed, 'To be returned to East India House', and No. 766, a drawing of the same subject as 765 is inscribed, 'To be returned to Dr Horsfield'.

765 and 766 are both drawings of the same subject, the *Neodon Sikimensis*. A specimen of this vole was sent to India House in 1852.

THOMAS HORSFIELD

1773–1859

1. (NHD 1. Nos. 76–172)

Ninety-seven drawings in water-colour, pencil, and pen-and-ink depicting 48 birds, 46 mammals and 2 reptilia from Java; bound in a volume measuring 21 by 14 inches. (Introduction, pages 46–8, Plate 5.)

Seventy of these drawings were probably made by Chinese artists in Java between 1811 and 1817, while the British were in occupation of the island. The drawing is, in some cases, weak and incompetent. They were received by the Library in August 1819.

Twenty-five pencil drawings (Nos. 126, 127, 129, 131–3, 135–7, 139, 141–3, 150, 151, 155, 156, 159–63, 165, 166 and 168) were made by William Daniell between 1820 and 1824 from Horsfield's stuffed specimens in the Company's Museum. Two water-colours (Nos. 147 and 164) for reasons of style would also appear to be by him. Twenty of the engravings in Horsfield's *Zoological Researches in Java and the Neighbouring Islands* (London, 1824) were made from these drawings: Plate 2 (No. 162), Plate 3 (No. 161), Plate 4 (No. 159), Plate 11 (No. 155), Plate 13 (No. 132), Plate 14 (No. 131), Plate 15 (No. 133 in reverse), Plate 16 (No. 135), Plate 17 (No. 136), Plate 20 (No. 129), Plate 21 (No. 139 with a slight alteration), Plate 23 (No. 126), Plate 26 (No. 141), Plate 29 (No. 150), Plate 30 (No. 156), Plate 31 (No. 168), Plate 33 (No. 165), Plate 67 (No. 137). Plates 27 and 28 appear to have been engraved by Daniell from the Javanese drawings Nos. 144 and 146 with slight modifications.

The drawings of birds were of assistance to Horsfield in preparing his 'Systematic Arrangement and Description of Birds from the Island of Java', a paper read to the Linnaean Society, 18th April 1820, XIIIth volume of *Transactions*, and in compiling his revised 'Catalogue of Birds' in *Zoological Researches*.

The drawings are of special interest since the Horsfieldian types were imperfectly preserved, and during the removal of the collections from Leadenhall Street to Fife House moths destroyed nearly the whole of them.

2. (NHD 9. Nos. 1401–1642)

Two hundred and forty-one drawings in water-colour, pen-and-ink and pencil; 236 depicting Lepidoptera and 5 cryptogams from Java; bound in a volume measuring 21 by 14 inches. (Introduction, pages 46–8.)

These drawings were collected by Horsfield in Java between 1811 and 1818. The drawings of mosses were probably made by himself, those of the insects by his local draughtsmen. The drawings of insects accompanied the specimens which he presented to the Company. They were used in preparing his *Descriptive Catalogue of the Lepidopterous Insects in the Company's Museum*, parts i and ii (1829) and for *A Catalogue of the Lepidopterous Insects in the Museum of the Hon. East India Company*, 2 vols. (London, 1857 and 1858–9) which he and his assistant Frederic Moore compiled together. The illustrations in the latter two volumes were made by J. O. Westwood (see page 27) from Horsfield's collection of drawings. The illustrations have been pasted into this album beside 59 of them.

The drawings are numbered 1–187 (some are duplicates) and are inscribed 'Java Horsfield' while the Latin name of the subject is also given. The drawings 1638–42 are inscribed 'Drawings of Java Mosses'.

Horsfield's botanical drawings were transferred to Kew in 1879. Unfortunately the working out of the botanical collections was entrusted to Robert Brown and the only result of all Horsfield's botanical research was Brown and Bennett's *Plantae Javanicae Rariores* (1838–52).

Horsfield presented his drawings to the Library when he retired from service in 1819 and became Keeper of the East India Company's Museum in Leadenhall Street from 1820–59. During that time he did much to order and catalogue the Company's collections.

SIR ALBERT HOWARD

1873–1947

(NHD 44/16, 17) Two water-colour drawings depicting cultivated and uncultivated *litchi* and *loquat* leaves, measuring 14 by 10 inches.

These drawings were made for Sir Albert Howard on 18th April 1921 by Indian painters employed by the Government of India at the Pusa Experiment Station in Bihar. Sir Albert worked there as First Economic Botanist from 1904–24. The drawings were made to illustrate his article 'The Effect of Grass on Trees', *Agricultural Journal of India*, XX, part iv, July 1925, reprinted from *Proceedings of the Royal Society*, Series B, XCVII, No. B. 683. The drawings were also reproduced in *Soil and Health*, Spring 1948, 40–1.

Lady Howard presented the drawings in 1955. They are of special interest in showing that Indian artists were still making natural history drawings for the Government as late as 1925.

EUDELIN DE JONVILLE

1. (MSS. Eur. E. 81. No. 199 in Kaye's *Catalogue of Eur. MSS.*)

One hundred and eighty-four folios in pencil and water-colour depicting plants of Ceylon bound in a volume measuring 15 inches by 10½. (Introduction, pages 34–8.)

This is the second of three volumes written and drawn by de Jonville entitled 'Quelques Notions sur L'Isle de Ceylan'. The drawings are made on Dutch paper with a 'C. & I. Honig' watermark. Twenty-four are unfinished and a line drawing of a fish is included on f. 126.

The drawings are numbered on the back 1–184 and each folio bears a description of the plant in pencil. Dissections are in many cases added. A number on the front relates 153 of the drawings to descriptions in the first volume of the set. (MSS. Eur. E. 80, pages 159–282.) In these cases the descriptions duplicate each other.

The first volume of the set records that the manuscript was 'Recd at Tellicherry. 3rd Nov. 1801. Presented by the Author.' The title page is inscribed, 'Colombo. Fevrier 1801.'

2. (MSS. Eur. E. 82. No. 199 in Kaye's *Catalogue of Eur. MSS.*)

Seventy-six folios in pencil, pen-and-ink and water-colour, bound in a volume measuring 15 by 10½ inches.

Sixty-nine ff. depict 2 mammals, 24 birds, 8 reptilia, 28 insects, 6 arthropods, while 7 ff. (70–6) depict a miscellaneous group including 1 mollusc, 2 echinoderms, 1 amphibia, 1 reptilia, 1 mammal and 1 fish.

On f. 74v there is a sketch in water-colour of a rock temple at Salsette inscribed 'Pagode taillée dans le Roc à Salcette'. This drawing was probably made when De Jonville passed through Bombay on his way to Ceylon in 1798. This is the third volume of the three written and drawn by de Jonville entitled 'Quelques Notions sur L'Ile de Ceylan'. The drawings are made on Dutch paper with a 'C. & I. Honig' watermark. They are described in the first volume of the series (MSS. Eur. E. 80). The descriptions of the mammals occur amongst the notes on 'Quadrupedes' pp. 291–300, the birds amongst those on 'Oiseaux' pp. 307–38, the reptiles amongst those on 'Reptiles' pp. 343–56 and the insects amongst those on 'Insectes', pp. 363–494.

The drawings reached the Library on 2nd June 1802. The Day Books record the receipt of 'Three Chests containing a Collection of Insects Shells, Minerals and other objects of Natural History, made at Ceylon by M. Jonville, accompanied by a Memoir in French and Sundry Drawings. Recd from the Baggage Warehouse. It is understood the above was sent as a Present to the Honble Company.' (North (see Ceylon Records 52) refers to the despatch of this MS. on 18th February 1801.) Various writers on de Jonville have been unaware of this collection. A copy of part of Vol. I, 'Narrative of a journey to Kandy made on the occasion of the Embassy of Major-General MacDowall in 1800', was purchased after the war in London and sent to Ceylon. A translation of it was published in the *Journal of the Ceylon Branch of the Royal Asiatic Society*, vol. 38, 1948.

JAMES KERR

1738–1782

(MSS. Eur. E. 11. No. 45 in Kaye's *Catalogue of Eur. MSS.*) Four drawings in water-colour depicting Indian plants and the lac insect; bound in a volume entitled 'Doctor Kerr's Observations upon Natural History'. (Introduction, page 6.)

These drawings, made for Kerr in the Bengal Presidency, illustrate three of his botanical papers which reached the Company in July 1777.

i. Mimosa Japonica, 12 by 14½ inches, illustrating 'A Description of a New Plant from which the Terra Japonica of the shops is extracted'.

ii. The flowers and fruit of 'The Prass Tree of Bengal' (*Butea frondosa*), 15 by 9 inches.

iii. A spray of leaves covered with lac. A lac insect (*coccus laccae*) is inset, 15 by 9 inches. These two drawings illustrate the 'History of the Coccus laccae', a paper which appears to have been published.

iv. The 'Burrum Chundalli' (*Desmodium gyrans* (L.) DC.), 16 by 14½ inches, illustrating the 'Description of a New and Singular Plant'.

The drawings appear to have been made by Indian painters.

JOHN LEYDEN

1775–1811

(NHD 40) Ninety-seven drawings in gouache depicting flowers, fruits and roots, measuring approx. 10¼ × 7¼ inches 'bound in a *muraqqa*' measuring 14 × 11 inches. (Introduction, pages 10–11.)

These drawings by an Indian artist were collected by Leyden while he was in India from 1803 to 1810. They were entered in the 'Catalogue of Dr John Leyden's Oriental Library, Calcutta, 1812' (MSS. Eur. D. 562/20) as 'Kitabi Tusweer, a Book of drawings of Plants'. They were received by the Library in 1824.

The paintings are inscribed with their vernacular names in the Persian script and the last page is inscribed '97 Oriental Drawings of Flowers & Fruits. Bibliotheca Leydeniana, 438'.

COLIN MACKENZIE

1754–1821

I. (NHD 37)

Eighty-three water-colour and pencil drawings (6 unfinished) depicting 22 fishes, 36 birds, 19 mammals and 6 reptilia bound in with blank paper to form an album of 144 ff. measuring 15 by 9¼ inches. (Introduction, pages 38–9.)

These drawings were mostly collected by MacKenzie between 1799 and 1809 during the survey of Mysore, a few were collected in Madras in 1816 and 1 (the pangolin) in Calcutta in 1819.

On the cover is the title 'Book 22. No. 4. Natural History'. The title page is inscribed 'C. McK. Drawings W. Cat. ccxxiii.4. This volume contains—Drawings,' and f. 3 'This Book Contains Seven Drawings of Fishes of various Oriental parts. Thirty Six Drawings of Birds, Seventeen Drawings of Quadrupeds, Five Drawings of Snakes &

Lizards, Two Drawings of a Lizard & of a Pangolin'. Additional drawings of fishes must have been added after this inscription was made for there are now 22 fishes in the album.

The paintings appear to be by several hands. Some (e.g. the pangolin) may be MacKenzie's own sketches with his own rough notes, but the majority are probably by his draughtsmen and are neatly inscribed by a copyist with numbers, names, place and date, measurements and notes on special features.

From the inscriptions most of the fishes appear to have been found in the 'Hoggree River' and 'Toombudra Rivers' and painted at Bellary in 1801, although one was painted in 1794 and another from the 'Cubbanee Rivers' in 1804. The birds are entitled 'The Birds of Bednore & Canara and the Western Ghaats. 1805 1806', but some are dated 1802, 1804, 1807 and 1810. 'Mysore' has been added in pencil after the title. The animals are dated 1804, 1805 and 1807, the reptiles 1803, 1805, 1806 and 1816, and the pangolin 1819.

Other drawings of fishes made for Mackenzie are in the Library of the Asiatic Society of Bengal.

2. (NHD 38)

Fifty drawings in water-colour, pencil and pen-and-ink (6 unfinished) depicting plants from the Carnatic. The drawings are bound in with blank paper to form an album of 53+ii ff. measuring 15 by 9¼ inches. (Introduction, pages 38–9.)

These drawings were collected in the Ballaghat and Canara districts between 1804 and 1807 while MacKenzie was engaged on the survey of Mysore and adjoining districts.

On the cover is the title 'No. 5. Drawings of Plants in the Carnatic–Balla-Ghaat & in the Canara from 1804 to 1807'. The title page is inscribed, 'C.McK.5. Drawings W.Cat. ccxxiii.5. Book 23,' and p. ii, 'Natural History of Mysore. Botany.' There follows on f.1 a 'List of the Botanical Drawings contained in this Book. No.5. Nos. 1–50'.

The paintings appear to be by several hands, probably MacKenzie's draughtsmen. The drawings are neatly inscribed with Latin and sometimes English names, space being left for the Sanskrit and Kanarese. Dates and places are given and occasionally measurements. In certain cases notes on the uses of the plant are provided, e.g. No. 48.

The two albums were received by the Library in July 1823 and listed by H. H. Wilson *The Mackenzie Collection* (Madras 1882) p. 581, Nos. 4 and 5. They received little attention, however, for no one, not even Horsfield, seems to have mentioned them in the catalogues of the Company's natural history collections.

A drawing of Talipot palm trees (*Corypha umbraculifera* L.) with an unusual inflorescence appears in MacKenzie's Portfolio 4, No. 55, 'Views at Poonah and in Orissa, Bengal and Upper Hindostan'. (*Western Drawings No.* 729.)

A further book of natural history drawings in the MacKenzie collection has not been identified. It is listed in Wilson's catalogue (p. 581) as 'Portfolio 6. Natural History' and it is described in the Library's list of MacKenzie's drawings (MSS. Eur. D. 562/3) which was made soon after their arrival in July 1823. It appears to have contained 74 drawings—10 animals, 16 birds, 15 fishes, 1 arthropod, 3 insects, 20 reptiles and 9 plants.

WILLIAM MARSDEN

1754–1836

(NHD 1. Nos. 1–31; NHD 2. Nos. 285, 300–2) Thirty-five drawings in pencil, pen-and-ink, and water-colour depicting 15 mammals, 5 birds, 5 fishes, 4 molluscs, 3 insects and 3 reptilia. (Introduction, pages 17–9, Plate 2.)

These drawings were collected by Marsden between 1784 and 1808 for a third edition (London, 1811) of the *History of Sumatra*. Eleven of its 27 plates were engraved from these drawings. Drawing No. 5 is the original of Plate XV, No. 8 of XII (1) (the animals being reversed and incorporated into a landscape), No. 9 of XIV (2), No. 10 forms the lower half of Plate XIII (2) and No. 11 the upper half, No. 12 of Plate XIV (1), No. 14 of XII (2), No. 15 of XI (1), No. 16 of X (1), No. 17 of XIII (1) reversed with a landscape added, No. 18 of the left-hand portion of IX reversed and No. 285 of the right-hand portion reversed, No. 26 of Plate X (2) reversed.

From inscriptions on certain of the drawings and on the engravings it is clear that the majority were made either by Chinese painters or by a Mr Bell, who may have been Dr William Bell, a Company surgeon in Sumatra in 1792. Drawings numbered 8, 17, 18, 26 and 285 are attributed to Chinese artists in the engravings; Nos. 2, 19–21, 25, 28–31 and 300–2 in the same style being probably also by them. No. 13 may well be a somewhat ambitious attempt by a Chinese painter to execute a landscape in the European manner. Drawings numbered 9–12, 14–16 are attributed in the engravings to 'Mr Bell' and No. 6 is inscribed 'Drawn by Mr Bell'. On grounds of style Nos. 1, 3, 7, 22–4 and 27 may also be by him. Drawing No. 5 is attributed in the engraving to de Jonville and No. 4 appears to be a copy made for Dr Marsden from the drawing in de Jonville's Collection, Vol. III, f. 7 (page 83). The note in French, 'For Dr Marsden', inserted between drawings No. 3 and 4, describing the hornbill of Ceylon was written by de Jonville. This naturalist had presented his collection to the Company on 2nd June 1802, and Marsden was almost certainly in correspondence with him. No. 25 is inscribed, 'From Pulo Pinang'.

At the time of the presentation of Marsden's drawings to the Library in 1836, incorrect attributions appear to have been inscribed on some of the drawings (e.g. Nos. 2 and 4, which are attributed to Bell). Of these the style of No. 2 is quite different from his, and No. 4 is by de Jonville.

John McClelland
1800–1883

(NHD 6. Nos. 811–996) One hundred and eighty-six drawings in pen-and-ink and water-colour depicting 173 birds (110 separate drawings and 63 duplicates), 12 mammals (9 separate drawings and 3 duplicates) and 1 mollusc from Assam, India. Seven drawings are unfinished. Bound in a volume measuring 21 by 14 inches. (Introduction pages 41–3.)

These drawings were made during August and September 1836, while McClelland was on an expedition with Drs Wallich and Griffith to report on the tea shrub in Assam.

Each picture is inscribed with the Latin and English name of the subject, as well as 'Assam Collection, 1836'. Sometimes the date on which the drawing was made is given. The receiving date, '1856', and 'McClelland' were added later. In 1846 the drawings appear to have been submitted by McClelland to Edward Blyth (see pages 12–3) who added notes and the initials 'E.B.' to some of the drawings of birds, e.g. No. 939.

The Collection was presented to the Library in August 1856. The specimens, from which the drawings had been made, and which had been presented to the Company in December 1841 and October 1843, are now largely decayed. The drawings are of importance for they include at least one type drawing, No. 871, inscribed '*Parus Griffithi*', the grey tit found by Dr Griffith during the expedition. See note by E. Blyth *Journal of the Asiatic Society of Bengal*, January–June 1847, XVI, I, 445: 'This species is founded on a drawing of a bird obtained by the late Dr Griffith, between Assam and Ava'.

Richard Parry
In the East 1793–1811

(NHD 2. Nos. 286–99) Fourteen drawings in water-colour depicting 12 birds, 1 mammal and 1 fish from Sumatra; bound in a volume measuring 21 by 14 inches. (Introduction, page 19. Plate 3.)

These drawings were collected by Parry while Resident of Fort Marlborough (Bencoolen) in Sumatra between 1807 and 1811.

Nos. 288, 290–4 and 297 are inscribed in Urdu, 'The painter of this picture is Manu Lal, artist, an inhabitant of Azimabad (Patna City)'. The style of the paintings is uniform, many of them characterized by a small patch of shaded grass on which the specimen stands, and it seems likely that all were painted by Manu Lal. The paper is watermarked 1806 and was probably brought from England by Parry on the expiry of his leave.

The date '26/6/1812' on No. 299 refers to Parry's presentation of the collection to the East India Company's Library on his retirement. The Company's first Day Book records this gift, 'June 26th, 1812. Recd from the Baggage Warehouse, per *Union* 202 Drawings of Plants. Mr Ricd Parry. Plants and Animals from Sumatra.' On 2nd December 1812, 52 duplicates were returned to him and 150 drawings retained. 125 paintings of plants were transferred to Kew in 1879.

THOMAS STAMFORD RAFFLES

1781–1826

(NHD 4. Nos. 537–665) One hundred and twenty-nine drawings in water-colour of birds from Sumatra bound in a volume measuring 21 by 14 inches. (Introduction, pages 15–7.)

These drawings were made in Sumatra in 1820 while Raffles was Resident there. No. 641 is inscribed, 'Sumatra' and '103. Sir St. R. Sumatra'. In many cases the vernacular names of the specimens are given. The drawings arrived in the Library in 1821 and accompanied the specimens which Raffles sent to the Company's Museum and which are now in the British Museum (Natural History).

JOHN FORBES ROYLE

1799–1858

(NHD 5. Nos. 770–804) Thirty-five drawings in water-colour and pencil depicting 17 birds, 5 mammals, 12 insects and 1 amphibia from northern India, bound in a volume measuring 21 by 14 inches. (Introduction, pages 25–7.)

The drawings of birds, mammals and amphibia were made at the Saharanpur Botanic Garden between 1823 and 1831. Those of insects were made in March 1835 by J. O. Westwood (1805–93), the famous Victorian entomologist, from the specimens which Royle had brought to England.

Some of these drawings are the originals of plates in Royle's *Illustrations of the Botany and other Branches of the Natural History of the Himalayan Mountains and the Flora of Cashmere* (London, 1833–9). No. 788 is the original of the upper part of Plate 5, No. 790 of the lower part. No. 786 is the original of the Honeysucker in Plate 7 and No. 780 of the Pitta in reverse. No. 773 and No. 774 in reverse appear in Plate 8. Insects Nos. 798, 793, 794 and 796 appear as numbers 4, 6, 5, 9 in Plate 9. Nos. 800–4 and 797, 795 and 799 appear as numbers 1, 2, 4, 8, 10, 7, 6, 9 in Plate 10.

The paintings of birds, mammals and amphibia appear to have been made by the team of Indian artists employed by Royle at the Saharanpur Garden, amongst whom was Lakshman Singh. His name appears on Nos. 780, 781 and 784.

RAJA SERFAGEE OF TANJORE

1777–1832

(NHD 7. Nos. 1001–1116 (a & b)) One hundred and seventeen drawings in water-colour and gouache depicting 30 birds, 1 falcon hood, 2 bird traps, 13 mammals, 38 fishes, 9 reptiles, 7 arthropods, 12 molluscs, 1 amphibia, 2 coelentrates, 1 vermes, 1 echinoderm from South India; bound in a volume measuring 21 by 14 inches. (Introduction, page 13–4. Plate 17.)

These drawings were rebound and entitled 'Mysore Drawings' *c.* 1879. They were, however, wrongly ascribed and are in fact the two volumes of 'The Natural Products of Hindostan painted under the direction of the Rajah of Tanjore and presented to the Court by Mr Benjamin Torin' in 1807. (See Introduction, page 13.) Benjamin Torin was a Company servant in Madras from 1779–1803, being Resident of Tanjore from 1800 to 1803. The paintings, made in about 1802, are by Indian artists, probably retained by the Raja himself. 1796 watermarks occur on some drawings.

WILLIAM HENRY SYKES

1790–1872

(MSS. Eur. D. 141. No. 379 in Kaye's *Catalogue of Eur. MSS.*) Nine water-colour drawings of plants from the Deccan, bound in a volume measuring 12½ by 8 inches entitled, 'No. 1. General and District Geographical Descriptions'. (Introduction, page 40.)

This volume is the first part of Sykes' 'First Report on Statistics of the Dukhun, 1826', which is inscribed, 'Transmitted by W. H. Sykes, Capn Offg Statl Reptr to Govt Bombay, 10th May, 1826'. It contains 9 drawings made to scale by Bombardier Llewellyn L. Fidlor of the 2nd Battalion, Bombay Artillery, who was Sykes' draughtsman. Fidlor (b. 1804), who reached India in 1824, gave his former occupation as 'Artist'.

The drawings are inscribed as follows, each plant having its name given in Marathi:

i. 'Jonesia Ashoka, or pinnata. Jaswunt or Wassungee or Ashoka.'

ii. 'An extraordinarily large Wuhr (Ficis indica) at the village of Mhow, Undur Mawul.' Syke's camp with tent and horses is shown under the tree.

iii. 'Peempree (Ficus—) embracing the Peempul (Ficus religiosa) at Ambolee Baum Ner.'

iv. 'Peempree. Ficus—embracing the Sawree (Bombax Neptaphyllum) and letting down roots from a branch at Choke in the Konkun Travellers' Bungalow.'

v. & vi. 'Medicinal Plants. Saal Phul, Boswellia thurifera. Astc Rechs. Gum olibanum Tree.'

vii. 'Peempul, Ficus religiosa with Lac upon it, the produce of the insect, Coccus laccus.'

viii. 'Spontaneous Plants. Wild Cinnamon. Jarhee Dalcheenee. Laurus cassia.'

ix. 'Indian Willow. Wallunj. Salix tetrasperma Rox.'

These drawings were made for Sykes between 1824 and 1826 during the period that he was Statistical Reporter to the Bombay Government and was engaged on a great survey of the Deccan, which occupied him from 1824 to 1831. His collection of specimens made during the survey was presented to the Museum on 23rd July 1831.

Most of Sykes' drawings are now in the British Museum (Natural History). There are 10 volumes of Manuscript Notes with a few small pencil or pen-and-ink sketches by Sykes himself as well as some water-colour drawings by Fidlor describing the Economic Plants and Agriculture of the Deccan. There are another 10 volumes of descriptions and observations on plants, animals and agricultural implements of the Deccan illustrated by over 280 water-colour drawings, as well as a small manuscript 'Reports on the Dakhan' with 21 drawings, dated Poona, 1 Jan. 1831.

NATHANIEL WALLICH

1786–1854

(NHD 5. Nos. 753–64; NHD 2. No. 304) Twelve water-colour drawings of 2 birds, 9 mammals (including 2 duplicates) and 1 insect from India, Nepal and Burma; bound in a volume measuring 21 by 14 inches. (Introduction, pages 23–5, 41–3.)

Nos. 757–9 and No. 304 were made during Wallich's plant-collecting expedition to Nepal in 1820–1. No. 759 is inscribed, 'Drawn from a specimen in the possession of the honbl. E. Gardner, Nepul 1821. Description & copy of this drawg sent down to Maj. Gen. Hardwicke.' Hardwicke and Wallich were great friends. No. 304 is a copy of this. Two duplicates, Nos. 757 and 758 (inscribed 'Cervus Wallichianus Cuv'), portray the *Cervus wallichii* which was seen in captivity by Wallich at Katmandu. No. 758 appears to be from his own collection. A similar stag was later sent to Barrackpore and described by Cuvier who had been sent a drawing from there.

Six other drawings were made on his expeditions to Burma in 1826 and 1827. (Nos. 753, 754, 760–3.) In 1826 he visited Prome, Ava, Rangoon and the Irrawaddy valley, and in 1827 Amherst, Moulmein, Martaban, Rangoon and Tenasserim. No. 753 is inscribed 'Prome, 1826', No. 754 'Amherst', No. 760 'Drawn by Vishnupersaud at the palace at Ava in Novemb. 1826. It is a very faithful representn,' No. 761 'On the Attran R., Martaban. See Attran Report,' No. 762 'Found among the ravines at Yenangeum on the Irrawaddy. Decr. 1826,' No. 763 'From Attran, in Martaban'.

Of the remaining pictures No. 764, an insect, is inscribed, 'Sent from the King of Oude with Bayley's letter, 1825'. A picture of a Gayal is attributed to Vishnu Prasad (No. 755), while No. 756 is a drawing of the same specimen by a Mr Berg Wolff; 'Drawn by Mr Berg Wolff from the same Gayal which Vishnpersaud drew'.

With the exception of No. 756, all the drawings are probably by Vishnu Prasad, one of the Company's draughtsmen employed at the Calcutta Botanic Garden who regularly went on tour with Wallich.

These drawings were part of a large collection of natural history specimens which reached the Library on 17th October 1828. The Day Book records the accession: 'Recd from Baggage Warehouse per Orient, Dr N. Wallich's collection of Natural Curiosities'.

MARQUIS WELLESLEY

1760–1842

(NHD 10–36) Two thousand six hundred and sixty folios of water-colour drawings, depicting plants, birds, quadrupeds, insects and fishes from India and the East Indies bound in 27 volumes measuring approx. 18 by 13 inches. (Introduction, pages 6–8, Frontispiece, Plates 1, 6, 7, 8, 11, 13, 15, 16, 20.)

There are 1617 folios (15 vols.) of plant drawings, 558 folios (6 vols.) of birds, 163 folios (2 vols.) of quadrupeds, 250 folios (2 vols.) of insects and 72 folios (1 vol.) of fishes. A few drawings are unfinished and are in outline only. One volume (NHD 23) contains an index to the plant drawings.

This collection was purchased by the India Office Library in 1866 for £50 from a certain J. Fletcher. Fletcher's exact identity is unknown but it is possible that he was J. F. Fletcher of Ashe, near Wrotham, Kent, father of James Fletcher (1852–1908), the Canadian entomologist and botanist.[1]

At the time of purchase, Fletcher stated that these drawings had originally been prepared in India for the Marquis Wellesley while he was Governor-General of Fort William from May 1798 to July 1805. There seems no reason to doubt this statement and the following facts corroborate it. Lord Wellesley had died in 1842, leaving no

[1] I am indebted to the late A. H. G. Alston of the British Museum (Natural History) for this information.

legitimate heir, and his possessions were sold in 1843. It is highly probable that his natural history collection passed into other hands at this time.

The drawings and index to the plants are all made on paper with watermarks varying from 1794 to 1802. At the same time various inscriptions link the collection closely to the Governor-General. Some (e.g. NHD 32, f. 7) appear to be by Wellesley himself and various specimens are recorded as being presented to him (NHD 32. f. 7) or as being in his possession (NHD 32. f. 108). It is difficult to identify handwriting as certain inscriptions were made in pencil and later inked in by a different hand. There are many references to people of the time, such as Dr John Fleming (NHD 32. f. 80). Two bird paintings (NHD 29. ff. 21 and 27) bear Lord Valentia's seal, and were probably given by him to Wellesley in 1802 during his visit to Calcutta. A number of plant drawings are copies of some belonging to Captain Hardwicke (1755–1835), a well-known amateur naturalist of the period.

There are also close links between this collection and that of Dr Buchanan, who was Wellesley's surgeon from 1803–1805. Many drawings of animals and birds are identical with those made under Buchanan's supervision at the Barrackpore Menagerie. The drawings of fishes are so similar to those in the surgeon's collection that they may well have been made by the same painter. The two volumes of plant drawings from Mysore and Nepal are copies of those made for Buchanan during his expeditions of 1800–1801 and 1802. It seems very probable that while attached to Wellesley's staff he assisted in building up the Governor-General's collection by obtaining duplicates for him, and some of the notes on the animal drawings may well be by Buchanan himself. One or two drawings bearing dates prior to Wellesley's arrival in India (e.g. NHD 32. f. 43) were perhaps from the same source. It is known that Buchanan assisted Sir John Anstruther to form his collection of drawings.

Similar links exist with Roxburgh. A number of plant drawings are copies of the Roxburgh *Icones* and were made at the Calcutta Garden by Roxburgh's team of painters. Many notes refer to the Garden (e.g. NHD 10. f. 48) and it is probable that some member of the staff named many drawings and compiled the index according to the Linnaean system.

Although a number of specimens depicted in these drawings were acquired from the East Indies, the majority of the inscriptions refer to Calcutta and Bengal and show an intimate connection with that part of India. The vernacular names are in Bengali and Hindi, and the Sanskrit form is sometimes given. The scripts used are Bengali, Nagari and Persian.

A few drawings appear to be by Chinese painters in Malaya (e.g. drawings of birds from Malacca, NHD 28, and plants from Penang, NHD 17). These were probably painted in Malaya and sent to Wellesley for his collection. The remainder, however, are almost certainly by Calcutta painters. Some of the finest drawings were probably executed by the Company's team of artists employed at the Botanic Garden and the Barrackpore

Menagerie. Others were done by painters, such as Mirza Sangi Beg and Manu Lal, who worked privately for the Marquis. It is impossible to attribute the drawings to particular artists, except in the few cases where there is an inscription, but it is easy to distinguish idioms and different degrees of skill. Some drawings are in pale water-colour, others are highly finished with meticulous over-painting and burnishing. Some of the birds stand on sharp-edged slabs of rock and soil; others are on a grassy strip running from margin to margin; others are contained within a frame and landscape.

The drawings were rebound after their acquisition by the Library and a uniform title-page inscribed on one of the blank sheets at the beginning of each volume: 'Originally prepared by Order of the Marquis Wellesley when Governor-General of India. See Council Minute dated 16th August, 1866'. Thirteen miscellaneous drawings and 37 drawings of insects appear to have been omitted and were later pasted into the natural history scrapbooks NHD 1 and 8. The edges of the folios were trimmed and some of the page numbers and inscriptions cut off. Various loose flower drawings were incorporated and the page numbers consequently interrupted so that they no longer correspond exactly with the original index. Recently many of the volumes have been rebound in blue morocco. At various times notes have been inscribed on the drawings correcting names, or giving references to publications (e.g. *Plants of the Coast of Coromandel*) where the Roxburgh originals have been reproduced or where references to the plants are made. In this way some confusion in the inscriptions has occurred and it is no longer possible to be entirely sure which are original and which later additions.

In the catalogue, a selection of inscriptions has been incorporated, which throw light on the sources of the collection or on Wellesley's interests.

I. Plants

(NHD 10. Volume I) $18\frac{1}{2}$ by 13 inches. 113 ff.: 112 ff. in water-colour and f. 99 an unfinished line drawing. 1794 watermark.

Folio 41, a copy of a drawing belonging to Captain Hardwicke; f. 48, 'N.Sp. from the island of Oma, flowered in the Bot. Garden. Augt. 1798'; f. 105, 'N.B. Of the culms of this grass the Hindus make their pens'.

(NHD 11. Supplement to Volume I) $18\frac{1}{2}$ by 13 inches. 118 ff. in water-colour. 1794 watermark.

Folio 4, 'From Pinang'; f. 63, 'From Chittagong'; ff. 76, 78, 'From Amboyna'; f. 79, 'From Pegu'; f. 87, 'Bengal spinach'; f. 98, 'Mr Farquhar is of opinion that the best Charcoal is made from this'; f. 100, 'N.S. Tipperah.'; f. 108, 'The leaves used in N.Circars to polish Ivory'.

(NHD 12. Volume II) $18\frac{1}{2}$ by 13 inches. 120 ff.: 119 in water-colour and f. 18 unfinished. 1794 watermark.

Folios 9, 62, 101, 116, 117, 119 copied from drawings belonging to Captain Hard-wicke; ff. 1, 118, 'From Pulo-pinang'; f. 5, 'From China'; ff. 26, 27, 115, 120, 'From New Holland'; f. 29, 'The berries small & taste like Water Cresses. The bark acrid & used by the Natives for blistering'; f. 30, 'The berries eatable, and the leaves much used in their Curries by the Natives of the Coast of Coromandel'; f. 42, 'The bark of the root used as a purgative in Bengal'; f. 43, 'The tender tops & leaves used in Curries'; f. 73, 'The nut used for purifying Muddy water'.

(NHD 13. Supplement to Volume II) 19 by 13½ inches. 108 ff. in water-colour. 1794 watermark.

Folio 17, 'Fld in Cal. Bot. Garden, 1798'; f. 19, 'N.S. . . . brought from Chittagong by Dr Buchanan'; f. 32, 'In Cal. Garden only'; f. 37, 'Brought from Amboyna, 1798'; f. 44, 'From Rungpore'; f. 58, 'Gulal being a Persian word & this flower never being used by the Hindus, the Plant is probably originally from Persia'; f. 65, 'The Andaman Red Wood for Furniture'; f. 74, 'From Napaul'.

(NHD 14 Volume III) 18½ by 13 inches. 112 ff. in water-colour. 1794 watermark.

Folio 32, a copy of a drawing belonging to Captain Hardwicke; f. 39, 'The young shoots used as food by the Hindoos'; f. 64, 'Water dock grows in abundance near Calcutta'; f. 93, 'Flowered in 1798 at Calcutta'; f. 100, 'From P. of Wales Island'.

(NHD 15. Supplement to Volume III) 19¼ by 13½ inches. 132 ff. in water-colour. 1801 watermark.

Folio 5, 'Seed from China'; f. 11. 'Grows in the N.E. hills of Bengal. The fruit watry and insipid'; f. 80, 'From the Isle of France'; ff. 91, 105, 126, 'From Amboyna'; f. 99, 'The common small mulberry on which the silkworms feed in Bengal'; f. 101, 'From China'; f. 108, 'From Travancore'; f. 124, 'From Rajemahl'.

(NHD 16. Volume IV) 18½ by 13 inches. 130 ff. in water-colour. 1794 watermark.

Folios 24, 26, 28, 81, 108, 109, 113 copies from drawings belonging to Captain Hardwicke; ff. 15, 52, 'In Calcutta Bot. Garden'; f. 19, 'China'; f. 25, 'From the Sunderbunds and is a very hard wood'; f. 27, 'From New Holland'; f. 115, 'The black seed much eaten by the natives'.

(NHD 17. Supplement to Volume IV) 18 by 12½ inches. 89 ff. in water-colour. 1794 watermark.

This volume contains a large number of plants from the East Indies. The first 23 ff. and ff. 27–68 were probably painted by Chinese artists in Malaya. ff. 47–68, 'Penang'; f. 81, 'Mysore'; f. 87, From Nepal; f. 89, From Sumatra.

(NHD 18. Volume V) 18½ by 13 inches. 106 ff.: 105 in water-colour and f. 27 an unfinished line drawing.

Folio 36, a copy of a drawing belonging to Captain Hardwicke; f. 10, 'Used as food by the natives, boiled in their Curries'; f. 21 'From Amboyna'; f. 96 'Lucknow, . . . 1799'; f. 103, 'The bark used for cordage'.

(NHD 19. Volume VI) 18½ by 13 inches. 125 ff. in water-colour.

Folio 106, a copy of a drawing belonging to Captain Hardwicke; f. 6, 'Common Bengal Cotton'; f. 7, 'Dacca Cotton'; f. 38, 'The Blackwood Tree used in India for making furniture'; f. 49, 'Esteemed in Bengal the best for Cordage'; f. 59, 'New Holland'; f. 78, 'Much used for Cattle'; f. 91, 'Found only in ye Bot. Garden'; f. 105, 'From Upper Hindostan'; f. 112, 'The seeds used as food'.

(NHD 20. Volume VII) 18 by 13 inches. 114 ff. in water-colour.

Folio 22, a copy of a drawing belonging to Captain Hardwicke; ff. 58, 77, 'Amboyna'; f. 61, 'This is the plant that Covers the Pools'; f. 66, 'Malacca'; f. 76, 'Bencoolen'; f. 80, 'Napaul'; f. 85, 'From Upper Hindostan'; f. 87, 'Penang'; f. 114, 'Isle of France'.

(NHD 21. Volume VIII) 18½ by 13 inches. 110 ff. in water-colour. 1794 watermark.

Folios 17 and 89 copies of drawings belonging to Captain Hardwicke; f. 16, 'From Prince of Wales Island'; f. 19, 'Held sacred by the Hindoos'; f. 83, 'Vulg. The Tody Tree & the Mode of straining the Juice. It is used as Yeast in Bengal & also when fermented as an intoxicating liquor.'; f. 91, 'Found only in the Botanic Garden.'; f. 96, 'Wild from Chittagong'.

(NHD 22. Volume IX) 18½ by 13 inches. 61 ff. in water-colour. 1794 watermark.

Two loose drawings inscribed 'Madras R.W.' have been inserted for comparative purposes at some time. These may possibly be drawings belonging to Robert Wight, the Madras Botanist.

Folios 50 and 51, probably Chinese drawings from Malacca. Folio 10 appears to be from a different source. 1796 watermark and a different hand describing the Babul Tree.

Folio 6, 'An Ardent Spirit is drawn from the Bark'; f. 19, 'The wood hard and Durable. Much used.'

(NHD 23. Index) 17 by 10½ inches. 56 pp.+ 8 pp. 1796 and 1802 watermarks.

An index arranged according to the Linnaeus Sexual system and also an alphabetical index of plants.

(NHD 24. Volume XIV) 19 by 12 inches. (The four supplements account for Vols. X–XIII.)

Eighty-four ff. depicting Mysore plants: 81 in water-colour and ff. 25, 51, 69, unfinished line drawings.

Inscribed on verso of title-page, 'All the plants in this Vol. as well as those marked B in the other Volumes are from Dr Buchanan's Mysore tour'. This inscription is probably in Wellesley's handwriting. 1796 and 1801 watermarks.

The word 'Copy' appears on several folios, e.g. ff. 9, 10, 16, and these drawings are probably copies of some made for Buchanan on his Mysore Tour of 1800–1.

(NHD 25. Volume XV) 19½ by 12 inches.

Ninety-six ff. depicting Nepal plants: 95 in water-colour, f. 57 unfinished line drawing. 1794 watermark.

These drawings appear to be copies of those made for Buchanan on his Nepal tour of 1802. Many drawings are inscribed 'B.N.' (Buchanan, Nepal).

II. Birds

(NHD 26. Volume I) 18½ by 13 inches. 120 ff. in water-colour.

Some of the drawings of parrots may be by Chinese painters. f. 17, 'Female Sparrow Hawk—Variety of my Calcutta sparrow hawk'; f. 40, 'From New South Wales'; f. 46, 'Malacca'; f. 54, 'Cassowara. In ye Possn of Mr Cowper'; ff. 89 and 103, from Chittagong.

(NHD 27. Volume II) 19 by 13 inches. 114 ff. in water-colour.

Folio 113 is similar to No. 276 by Gurudayal in the 'G & B' Collection; f. 10, 'In possn of Mr Cowper'; f. 13, 'From Gorruckpore'; ff. 17, 18, 19, 28, 36, 43, 'Malacca'. (These drawings are probably by Chinese painters); ff. 23, 40, 70, 'Calcutta'; f. 24. 'Sumatra Pigeon'. (This drawing is probably by a Chinese painter.)

(NHD 28. Volume III) 19 by 13 inches. 95 ff. in water-colour.

Folios 93–5 are drawings of skins of birds from the 'E. Islands'. Cf. 'G & B' Collection, No. 282 and f. 95 which may well have been painted from the same specimen. Compare also f. 81 and No. 213, 'G & B' Collection by Mahangu Lal.

Folio 2, 'Drawn from life in the possession of Mr Cowper, who told me he has known this Bird for twenty years. When he knew it first it was of the common colour of the Pelican of the Ganges'; f. 6, 'Drawn from Life in the possession of Marquis Wellesley'; f. 8, 'Found at Chittagong & Bhauglpore'; f. 11, 'This bird was bred by Mr Fombelle, then Judge at Bhauglepore, between a hen & a Peacock. The form of the feet was owing to an accident, it having when young been drawn into the fire by an Idle Boy. This account from Mr Fombelle himself'; f. 14, From 'Chittegong Hills. The drawing was taken on the 28th Augt., 1801'; f. 66, 'Drawn from Life by J. Thornton Esq.'; ff. 77, 84, 85, 87, 88, 'Malacca' (probably by Chinese painters); f. 89, 'At Goulparah'.

(NHD 29. Volume IV) 19 by 12 inches. 100 ff. in water-colour.

Folios 21 and 27 must have been given to Wellesley by Lord Valentia as they bear his Persian seal on the reverse. 'The Right Honourable Lord Bahadur Viscount Valentia, 1217' (i.e. 1802); ff. 25, 31, 40, 41, 43, 57 are probably by Chinese painters; f. 70v, 'From Life in Lord Wellesley's possn. The female is very like the English hen Pheasant only smaller'; f. 71, 'From Java'; f. 73, 'From Nepaul'; ff. 80 and 87, 'Found in the

Snowy mountains of Surinagur'; f. 84, 'From near Lucknow'. Hardwicke had recently been to Srinagar and Kumaon and these are almost certainly some of his drawings.

(NHD 30. Volume V) 16½ by 11½ inches. 70 ff. in water-colour. 1796 watermark.

(NHD 31. Volume VI) 14¾ by 11 inches. 59 ff. in water-colour. 1794 and 1801 watermarks.

III. QUADRUPEDS

(NHD 32. Volume I) 19 by 12 inches. 117 ff. in water-colour.

Folio 75 is a copy of No. 505 in the Buchanan Collection; f. 7, an inscription perhaps by Wellesley: 'W.1802'; f. 13, 'A Tyger Cat from Rohilcind'; f. 24, 'Drawn from the life 1st June, 1793 from one sent from Chittagong by Mr Crommelin'; f. 43, 'Drawn from the life. 1794'; f. 46, 'From the life, about nine months old—in the possession of the Earl of Mornington'; f. 55v, 'These drawings are from life in the possession of Marquis Wellesley'; ff. 77, 'From the Mongheer hills'; f. 80, 'From Life in possession of J. Fleming Esq.'; f. 81, 'Artist Manu Lal, the painter of Azimabad'; f. 85v, 'The Building is a small Chapel belonging to the Malabar Christians, a place of great sanctity & resorted to by many thousands of them annually on the first Sunday after Easter'; f. 90, 'From Coimbitoore'; f. 103v, 'From New Holland. . . . From a live specimen in the possession of Marquis Wellesley'; f. 107, 'In the possession of Mr. Hare'; f. 108v, 'In the possession of Marquis Wellesley'; f. 106 is probably by a Chinese painter.

(NHD 33. Volume II) 18½ by 11½ inches. 46 ff. in water-colour.

A large number of the drawings in this volume are copies of Buchanan's Barrackpore drawings. The following are examples: f. 2 and No. 480; f. 3 and No. 484; f. 11 and No. 488; f. 13 and No. 489; f. 19 and No. 510; f. 24 and No. 512; f. 25 and No. 511; f. 27 and No. 509; f. 31 and No. 504; f. 37 and No. 506; f. 42 and No. 496; f. 43 and No. 493; f. 44 and No. 492; f. 45 and No. 499.

Folio 2, 'From life—sent from the Coast of Malabar . . . a similar one was killed at Nattore in Bengal'; f. 11, 'From Chittagong'; f. 39, 'An Abyssinian Ram, brought to Calcutta from the Coast of Arabia—in the possn of John Thornhill, Esq.'; f. 40v, 'Coola, an animal of the Oppossum Tribe from New South Wales'.

IV. INSECTS

(NHD 34. Volume I) 17½ by 11½ inches. 131 ff. in water-colour depicting insects both life-size and enlarged. Two enlarged dissections are included. No inscriptions.

(NHD 35. Volume II) 17½ by 11½ inches. 119 ff. in water-colour depicting insects both life-size and enlarged. Inscription in Nagari on f. 98 and a few Latin names have been added at a later date.

V. Fishes

(NHD 36) 18½ by 12 inches. 72 ff. in water-colour depicting Indian fishes. 1794 water-mark. A dorsal view and dissections are sometimes given in addition to the lateral view. In addition to the Latin name, the vernacular name in Persian and Roman scripts is also given.

These paintings are very similar to those in Dr Buchanan's Collection (MSS. Eur. E. 72) and may well have been made for Wellesley by Buchanan's painter. Some drawings are almost identical. Compare Wellesley ff. 15 and 30 with ff. 46 and 39 Buchanan.

First Supplementary Collection

(NHD 1. Nos. 173–85) Thirteen drawings in water-colour depicting 4 mammals, a limb, tusks etc. of musk deer, 1 bird and 7 reptilia from India; bound in a volume measuring 21 by 14 inches.

These drawings were purchased on 16th August 1866 together with the main collection.

From the inscriptions Nos. 184 and 185 appear to have come from Madras and Nos. 180 and 181 from Calcutta. No. 180 is inscribed, 'Musk deer. Natural size in possession of J. Fleming Esqre, Calcutta'. (see page 23). No. 174 is inscribed in Urdu, 'This animal is found in Chītkām in Kohistan. Its name is rūpīya mīdah (chamelion). Dated 28th August, Christian year 1801. The work of Mirza Sangi Beg'. No. 175 is inscribed, 'This animal is found in Chītkām in Kohistan. Its name is sāṅdā (a species of sand-lizard). Dated 28th August, Christian year 1801. The work of Mirza Sangi Beg'. No. 176 is inscribed, 'The name of this animal is Goh (a species of iguana) and is found in this country. From snout to skull—6 inches. From skull to tail—4 ft 6 inches. From back to belly—6 inches. Work of Mirza Sangi Beg. Dated 28th August, Christian year 1801'. It is possible that 'Kohistan-i-chītkām' refers to the Chittagong Hill Tracts.

Second Supplementary Collection

(NHD 8. Nos. 1335–71) Thirty-seven drawings in water-colour depicting Indian insects; bound in a volume measuring 21 by 14 inches.

These drawings, entitled 'Miscellaneous', bear no inscription but stylistically appear identical with the drawings of insects in the Wellesley Collection (NHD 34 and 35). While there is no proof of provenance, there is every likelihood that they formed part of the first Wellesley Supplementary Collection (NHD 1, Nos. 173–85).

Catalogue

Miscellaneous Drawings

ANDREW LEITH ADAMS

(NHD 8. No. 1316) A drawing in water-colour depicting a 'Markhoa' (*Capra Magaceros*) by Dr A. L. Adams, presented in July 1856. The drawing is accompanied by a note from Adams describing the specimen and relating how it was killed in the Pir Panjal Range in Kashmir on 16th July 1854. Adams was a medical officer of the 22nd Foot in India from 1849 to 1873. He was stationed at Poona, Karachi and Rawalpindi, and made expeditions to the Himalayas and Kashmir. He contributed to the *Proceedings of the Zoological Society*. On leaving India he was stationed in Egypt and Canada, and after his retirement from the Army he became Professor of Zoology at Cork.

MICHAEL ATKINSON

(Home Miscellaneous Series, 375, pp. 268–74) Four water-colour drawings, measuring 15 by 9½ inches, depicting Hemp and Flax Plants, (i) 'Ghore Sun', (ii) 'Cooch Murdun Paat', (iii) 'Amleeah Paat', (iv) 'Sanchee Paat'. These drawings, made by Indian draughtsmen, accompanied a note on the cultivation of flax and hemp in Bengal submitted by Michael Atkinson, the Resident of 'Jungypore', on 21st November 1792. It was transmitted in 1793 from Bengal under the Court's Orders of 6th May 1791. This note and drawings have been bound up with other papers (see page 102) to form 'Correspondence relative to the Cultivation of Hemp and Flax from 1791–9', Home Miscellaneous Series, 375, pp. 1–468.

ANON

1. (NHD 2. Nos. 306, 308 and 310)

These water-colours depicting a bird, a mammal and a reptile, bear no inscriptions and cannot be accurately associated with any collection.

No. 306 on stylistic grounds may be part of the 'G & B' Collection.

2. (NHD 8. Nos. 1293 and 1294)

Two water-colour drawings of snakes. The first is inscribed, 'Drawn by Hurrish Chunder Khan. Student. Gov^t Sch: of Art, Calcutta. Specimen in Indian Museum'. The technique is purely European. It is not known when or by whom these drawings

99

were sent to the Library, but the Calcutta Art School was founded in 1854 and the drawings may have been made soon after. It is possible that they were part of Cantor's collection.

3. (NHD 8. Nos. 1325–34)
    Ten water-colour drawings depicting insects probably from Madras, since they are inscribed 'Madras'. The drawings have been cut out and stuck on to larger sheets.

4. (NHD 42)
    Ten drawings in water-colour depicting fruits with their leaves and blossom probably from Sumatra, measuring approx. 16 by 21 inches and bound in a volume measuring 19 by 23½ inches. A bird is included in the last two drawings (Introduction, pages 59–61, Plate 12).
    These paintings are by a Chinese artist probably from Sumatra and are executed on English paper with an 1807 watermark. They were probably made about 1808. There is no record for whom they were made or when they were acquired by the Library, but they appear to have been borrowed by the Marsdens in 1809. Six drawings of fruits which correspond to these were 'Feb. 22nd, 1809. Taken by Mr Wilkins for Mrs Marsden' and returned on 2nd October. On 24th February Marsden himself took away two more drawings. Folio 4 depicting a 'Mangustin' is very similar to Plate 3 of his Sumatra illustrations and it seems probable that Mrs Marsden (née Wilkins), who made this and several other drawings for her husband's book, adapted these drawings.

5. (NHD 43)
    A volume measuring 18 by 14 inches containing:
    (i) 12 water-colour drawings of fruit, vegetables and flowers, and
    (ii) 24 water-colour drawings of insects on a small spray in their various stages of development, both measuring approx. 9½ by 7½ inches (ff. 1–36).
    (iii) 62 water-colour drawings (ff. 37–98) mainly of insects (including silk-worms at different stages of development), but also of amphibia, arthropods, reptilia and molluscs (ff. 50, 53, 60, 64, 66, 86, 96).
    (iv) 18 water-colour drawings of insects on a large spray of flowers (ff. 99–116).
    These drawings, made by Chinese artists, are on English paper with an 1805 watermark (Introduction, pages 59–61, Plates 6, 21, 22).

EDWARD ROUTH BLAGRAVE
1831–1863

(NHD 41) Seventy-nine drawings in gouache depicting Indian birds, bound in a volume measuring 7½ by 6 inches.

Catalogue

These drawings, in a broken-down Mughal style, were probably made in the Punjab *c.* 1840 by an Indian artist. Each folio is inscribed with the name of the bird in Latin, Urdu and a Punjabi script. In certain drawings the painter preserves some of the vigour with which these birds are rendered in Indian miniatures (e.g. the peacock, f. 33), but he is at a loss when depicting less familiar types (e.g. f. 63).

This volume was presented to the Library in October 1857 by a Captain Blagrave and is inscribed 'Drawings of Indian Birds. Presented by Captain Blagrave. Oct. 1857'. A Captain Edward Routh Blagrave (1831–1863), the son of Charles George Blagrave of the Company's Bengal Civil Service (1804–1836), served with the Madras Engineers from 1851–63. If he is the donor of the drawings, however, it is unlikely that they were made specially for him since the Punjabi inscriptions would suggest a northern Indian provenance.

COURT

(NHD 2. No. 303) A water-colour drawing depicting 1 amphibia inscribed, 'Capt. Court. Sept 13. 1819'.

This may be Captain H. Court, a Madras artillery officer who was in India from 1799 to May 1819 or Captain Charles Court of the Bombay Marine Service, in India 1789 to 1821. Court's collection of plant drawings was transferred to Kew in 1879 and this is the only drawing which has remained in the India Office Library. It appears to be by an Indian painter.

JOHN BENNET HEARSEY

1793–1865

(NHD 2. No. 309) One drawing in water-colour of a fish. Inscribed, 'Natural size. Found beyond the rivers above Gurdope, Tartary. Found in hundreds, will take any insect in the shape of a fly'.

Sir John Hearsey, who was born in India, served in Bundelkund, Rewa, in the Pindari and Mahratta Wars, and at Bharatpur, Dig, Chilianwala and Gujerat. He helped suppress the Barrackpore and 1857 Mutinies. He commanded the 6th Bengal Light Cavalry and later the 21st Hussars.

JOHNSON

(NHD 2. No. 305) A water-colour drawing of a bird inscribed, 'From Mr Johnson's collection of MSS. etc.' If this refers to the collection of Richard Johnson, who was in India from 1770–90 and whose fine oriental miniatures and manuscripts were purchased by the Company, it may well prove to be the oldest bird drawing in the Library. It appears to be by an Indian artist, perhaps from Lucknow, where Johnson spent some years.

WILLIAM ROXBURGH

1. (Home Miscellaneous Series, 375, page 374).

A water-colour drawing of a Flax Plant (*Aletris Nervosus*) with dissections measuring 18½ by 12 inches accompanying a letter sent by Dr Roxburgh from Samalkot on 1st February 1793 to the Court of Directors entitled, 'A Botanical Description and Drawing of a new Species of Flax-plant with a few Observations thereon'.

This drawing was made by one of Roxburgh's Indian draughtsmen at Samalkot.

2. (Home Miscellaneous Series, 375, pp. 255, 257, 259, 261).

Four water-colour drawings, measuring 18 by 12 inches, inscribed:
   (i) *Corchorus olitorius Linn.* No. 901.
   (ii) *Corchorus capsularis Linn.* No. 902.
   (iii) *Corchorus fuscus.* No. 903.
   (iv) *Aeschynomene cannabina* of Konig. No. 904.

These drawings accompany a letter sent by Roxburgh to the Court of Directors from Calcutta on 23rd December 1794, concerning 'A Botanical History of the (Paat & Dooncha) Hemp and Flax Plants of Bengal, with the mode of cultivation and manufacture'. They were probably made by Roxburgh's Indian draughtsmen at the Calcutta Garden.

The drawings and letters under 1 and 2 above have been bound up with other papers (see page 99) to form 'Correspondence relative to the Cultivation of Hemp and Flax from 1791–9', (Home Miscellaneous Series, 375, pp. 1–468).

SAMUEL NEVILL WARD

(NHD 2. No. 307) A water-colour drawing (unfinished) of a wild cat, inscribed 'S. N. Ward. Canara'.

Samuel Nevill Ward was a member of the Madras Civil Service from 1831–63. He served in Canara in 1837 as Registrar of the Zillah Court and in 1843 and from 1845–47 as Acting Sub-Collector and Joint Magistrate. He was a well-known amateur naturalist. He presented specimens to the Company's Museum, and Horsfield refers to his insect collection in Part II of the Catalogue to the Museum's collection of Lepidopterous Insects. This drawing, apparently made by himself, may have been presented to the Museum when he went on leave in 1847.

SELECT BIBLIOGRAPHY

I. Manuscript Sources

For manuscripts of catalogues, lists, and books by collectors of drawings represented in the Library see Bibliography III

British Museum (Natural History)
Botanical Department
   One hundred and sixteen paintings of plants. MSS. 581·9(54)F.

British Museum (Natural History)
Zoological Department
   Two volumes of lists of Collections by:
   1. Harris, Falconer, Lovell, Bax, Hodgson, Hope, Richardson, Taylor, Moore, Carter, Buckley, Strachey, Westwood, Jones, James, Gould, Tytler, Royle, Thompson, Morris, Schlagintweit, Downes.
   2. Horsfield, Raffles, Vigors, Finlayson, Hardwicke, Herbert, Wallich, Wight, Sykes, Reeves, Blyth.
   These two volumes (MSS. 89 f. I) contain various catalogues and memoranda transferred from the Library to the British Museum in 1859 to 1860 and 1879 to 1880.

Commonwealth Relations Office
East India Company Records
   Court Minutes, vol. 116 (8th April 1807 to 13th April 1808).
   Ceylon Records, vol. 4 (4th May 1799 to 30th April 1800); vol. 5 (2nd May to 30th November 1800); vol. 6 (1st December 1800 to 28th April 1801); vol. 11 (1st May 1799 to 12th April

Commonwealth Relations Office *(cont.)*
East India Company Records (cont.)
   1800); vol. 52 (25th May 1798 to 31st December 1801); vol. 53 (1797–1802).

India Office Library
   Day Books: 1801–14, 1814–20, 1820–3, 1823–9, 1829–37, 1838–47, 1847–53, 1853–8, 1858–67. MSS. Eur. E.239/1–9.
   Various lists and correspondence relating to manuscripts and drawings acquired by the East India Company's Library (MSS. Eur. D. 562/3, 16, 20, 21–28).
   Roxburgh Manuscripts: nos. 144–6 (23 vols.) and 148 and 149 (2 vols.) in Kaye's *Catalogue of Manuscripts in European Languages*, ii, part ii, section I (London, 1937).
   'Some Remarks on the Soil and Cultivation on the Western Side of the River Hoogly'. A survey of the land, part of which formed the Company's Botanic Garden. By Lieutenant-Colonel Robert Kyd. MSS. Eur. F. 95.

Victoria and Albert Museum
Indian Section
   Smith, R., 'Pictorial Journal of Travels in Hindustan from 1828 to 1833'. I.M. 15–1915.

II. Printed Books

ANNESLEY, G. (Lord Valentia). *Voyages and Travels to India, Ceylon, the Red Sea, Abyssinia and Egypt in 1802–6*, 3 vols. (London, 1809).

ARBERRY, A. J. *The Library of the India Office* (London, 1938).

ARCHER, MILDRED. 'British Patrons of Indian Artists', *Country Life*, 18th August 1955.
——'Indian Paintings for British Naturalists', *The Geographical Magazine*, September 1955.

ARCHER, MILDRED and W. G. *Indian Painting for the British* (London, 1955).

ARCHER, W. G. *Bazaar Paintings of Calcutta* (London, 1953).

BISWAS, K. (ed.) Royal Botanic Garden, Calcutta, 150th Anniversary Volume, parts i and ii, 1942.

BLUNT, W. *The Art of Botanical Illustration* (London, 1950).

BRITISH MUSEUM. *The History of the Collections contained in the Natural History Departments of the British Museum*, 2 vols. (London, 1904, 1906).

BURKILL, I. H. 'Chapters on the History of Botany in India', part i, *Journal of the Bombay Natural History Society*, LI, No. 4, 1953, 846–78; part ii, *Journal of the Bombay Natural History Society*, LIV, No. 1, 1956, 42–86.

CORDINER, J. *A Description of Ceylon*, 2 vols. (London, 1807).

CRAWFORD, D. G. *Roll of the Indian Medical Service, 1615–1930* (London, 1930).

CRAWFURD, J. *Journal of an Embassy from the Governor-General of India to the Courts of Siam and Cochin China* (London, 1828).

CURZON, G. N. (Marquess Curzon of Kedleston) *British Government in India: the Story of the Viceroys and Government Houses*, 2 vols. (London, 1925).

DODWELL, E. & MILES, J. S. *Alphabetical List of the Honble. East India Company's Bengal Civil Servants, 1780–1838* (London, 1839).
——*Alphabetical List of the Officers of the Indian Army* (London, 1838).

FORBES, J. *Oriental Memoirs*, 2 vols. (London, 1813).

GOLD, C. *Oriental Drawings* (London, 1806).

GRAHAM, MARIA (Lady Callcott). *Journal of a Residence in India* (Edinburgh, 1812).

HOOKER, J. D. 'A Century of Indian Orchids', *Annals of the Royal Botanic Garden, Calcutta*, V, part i, 1905.

HORA, S. L. 'On the Manuscript Drawings of Fish in the Library of the Asiatic Society of Bengal', *Journal and Proceedings of the Asiatic Society of Bengal*, XXII, 1926, No. 3, 99–115.

HUNTER, W. W. *Life of Brian Houghton Hodgson* (London, 1896).

JARDINE, W. *Memoirs of Hugh Edwin Strickland* (London, 1858).

JOURDAIN, MARGARET and JENYNS, R. S. *Chinese Export Art in the Eighteenth Century* (London, 1950).

KAYE, G. R. *Catalogue of Manuscripts in European Languages in the India Office Library*, ii, part ii: Minor collections and miscellaneous manuscripts; section I (London, 1937).

KINNEAR, N. 'The History of Indian Mammalogy and Ornithology, part i, *Journal of the Bombay Natural History Society*, L, No. 4, 1952, 766–778; part ii, *Journal of the Bombay Natural History Society*, LI, No. 1, 1953, 105–10.

MARTIN, R. M. (ed.) *The Despatches, Minutes and Correspondence of the Marquess Wellesley during his Administration in India*, 2nd ed., iv (London, 1837).

PERCIVAL, R. *An Account of the Island of Ceylon* (London, 1803).

PHILLIMORE, R. H. *Historical Records of the Survey of India*, 4 vols. (Dehra Dun, 1946–59).

PIERIS, P. E. 'MacDowall's Embassy, 1800', *Journal of the Ceylon Branch of the Royal Asiatic Society*, XXXVIII, 1948.

PRAIN, D. 'A Sketch of the Life of Francis Hamilton (once Buchanan)', *Annals of the Royal Botanic Garden, Calcutta*, X, part ii, 1905.

PRINSEP, H. T. *A General Register of the Honourable East India Company's Civil Servants of the Bengal Establishment, 1790–1842* (Calcutta, 1844).

RAFFLES, SOPHIA, LADY. *Memoir of the Life and Public Services of Sir Thomas Stamford Raffles* (London, 1830).

RUSSELL, P. *An Account of Indian Serpents*, 2 vols. (London, 1796).
——*Descriptions and Figures of Two Hundred Fishes collected at Vizagapatam on the Coast of Coromandel*, 2 vols. (London, 1803).

SEALY, J. R. 'The Roxburgh Flora Indica Drawings at Kew', *Kew Bulletin*, No. 2 and No. 3, 1956.

STANSFIELD, H. 'The Royle Herbarium', *The North Western Naturalist*, June 1953.
——'Plant Collecting in the Himalayas', *Liverpool Bulletin*, III, No. 3, March 1954.

SYNGE, P. M. 'Chinese Flower Paintings', *Journal of the Royal Horticultural Society*, LXXVIII, part vi, June 1953, 209–13.

TENNENT, J. E. *Ceylon*, 2 vols. (London, 1859).

WATT, G. *A Dictionary of the Economic Products of India*, vi, part iii (London, 1893).

WESTWOOD, J. O. Obituary of, *Entomologists' Monthly Magazine*, 1893.

WIGHT, R. and WALKER-ARNOTT, G. A. *Prodromus Florae. Pens. Ind. Or.* (London, 1834).

WILSON, H. H. *The Mackenzie Collection* 2nd ed. (Madras, 1882).

WURTZBURG, C. E. *Raffles of the Eastern Isles* (London, 1954).

III. SELECT WRITINGS BY COLLECTORS

ADAMS, A. L. 'Notes on the habits, etc. of a few animals of various parts of Hindustan and the Western Himalayan Mountains', *Edinburgh New Philological Journal*, VIII, 1858, 253–63.

——'Remarks on the habits and haunts of some of the Mammalia found in various parts of India and the Western Himalayan Mountains', *Proceedings of the Zoological Society, London*, XXVI, 1858, 512–31.

——*Wanderings of a Naturalist in India, the Western Himalayas, and Cashmere* (Edinburgh, 1867).

BLYTH, E. *Catalogue of the Birds in the Museum of the Asiatic Society, Calcutta* (Calcutta, 1849).

——*Catalogue of the Mammalia in the Museum of the Asiatic Society, Calcutta* (Calcutta, 1863).

——'A Catalogue of the Mammals and Birds of Burma', *Journal of the Asiatic Society of Bengal*, part ii, August 1875. Extra Number. (This number also includes a Memoir of Blyth by A. Grote and a complete list of his papers.)

BUCHANAN, F. (*later* BUCHANAN-HAMILTON). *An Account of the Fishes found in the River Ganges and its Branches* (Edinburgh, 1822).

——*A Journey from Madras through the Countries of Mysore, Canara and Malabar*, 3 vols. (London, 1807).

——*A Geographical, Statistical and Historical Description of the District . . . of Dinajpur in the . . . Province of Bengal, 1807–8* (Calcutta, 1833).

BUCHANAN, F. (*later* BUCHANAN-HAMILTON) (*cont.*)

——*An Account of the District of Purnea in 1809–10*, ed. V. H. Jackson (Patna, 1928).

——*An Account of the District of Shahabad in 1809–10* (Patna, 1934).

——*An Account of the District of Bhagalpur in 1810–11*, ed. A. Banerji-Sastri (Patna, 1939).

——*An Account of the Kingdom of Nepal and of the Territories annexed to this dominion by the House of Gorkha* (Edinburgh, 1819).

——(*With* W. L. Gibbons) Descriptions of animals and birds in the Barrackpur Menagerie (*MSS. Eur. D. 94 and MSS. Eur. D. 541*).

——A Description of the Gangetic Fishes (*MSS. Eur. E. 71*).

——Original Notes concerning the Gangetic Fishes (*MSS. Eur. E. 70*).

CANTOR, T. E. 'General Features of Chusan', *Annals and Magazine of Natural History*, IX, 1842, 265–78, 361–71, 481–94.

——*The Zoology of Chusan* (Calcutta, 1842).

——'Catalogue of Mammalia inhabiting the Malayan Peninsula and Islands', *Journal of the Asiatic Society of Bengal*, XV, 1846, 171–203, 241–79.

——'Catalogue of Reptiles inhabiting the Malayan Peninsular and Islands', *Journal of the Asiatic Society of Bengal*, XVI, 1847, 607–56, 897–952, 1026–78.

——'Catalogue of Malayan Fishes', *Journal of the Asiatic Society of Bengal*, XVIII, 1849, 983–1422.

DAY, F. *The Land of the Permauls; or, Cochin, its Past and its Present* (Madras, 1863).

——'On the Fishes of Cochin on the Malabar Coast of India', *Proceedings o, the Zoological Society of London*, part i, 1865, 2–40; part ii, 1865, 286–318.

——*The Fishes of Malabar* (London, 1865).

——*Report on the Freshwater Fish and Fisheries of India* (Calcutta, 1873).

——*Report on the Sea Fish and Fisheries of India and Burma* (Calcutta, 1873).

——*On the Fishes of Yarkand* (London, 1876).

——*The Fishes of India, Burma and Ceylon*, 2 vols. (London, 1876–8).

——*Ichthyology* (Calcutta, 1878).

——*Fishes*, 2 vols. (London, 1889).

FINLAYSON, G. *The Mission to Siam, and Hué, the capital of Cochin China, in the years 1821–2, from the Journal of the late George Finlayson, Esq*, ed. S. Raffles (London, 1826).

——Mission to Siam (*MSS. Eur. D. 135*).

——Lists of Collections made during his Mission to Siam (*MSS. Eur. D. 136*).

GRIFFITH, W. *Icones Plantarum Asiaticarum*, 2 vols. (London, 1847–54).

——*Notulae ad Plantas Asiaticas* (London, 1847–54).

——*Journals of Travels in Assam, Burma, Bootan, Affghanistan and the neighbouring countries, and Itinerary notes on Plants collected in the Khasyah and Bootan Mountains, 1837–8, in Affghanistan and neighbouring countries, 1839–41*. Arranged by J. McClelland, 2 vols. (London, 1847).

——'Report on the Tea Plant of Upper Assam', *Transactions of the Agric. and Hortic. Soc. of India*, V, 1838, 94–180.

GRIFFITH, W. (*cont.*)

——'Report on the Tea Plant of Upper Assam', *Madras Journal*, VIII, 1838, 348–369.

——'Extracts from a report on subjects connected with Afghanistan', *Ann. Nat. Hist.* X, 1842, 190–6.

——Report on the Productions of Afghanistan (*MSS. Eur. D. 159*).

HEYNE, B. *Tracts, Historical and Statistical, on India, with journals of several tours through various parts of the Peninsula; also an account of Sumatra, in a series of letters* (London, 1814).

HODGSON, B. H. 'On the Rats, Mice, and Shrews of the central region of Nepal', *Ann. Nat. Hist.* XV, 1845, 266–70.

(For a list of his 140 papers see *Catalogue of Scientific Papers 1800–1863*, Royal Society of London, iii (London, 1869))

HORSFIELD, T. 'Systematic Arrangement and Description of Birds from the Island of Java', *Transactions of the Linnaean Society*, XIII, April 1822, 133–200.

——*Zoological Researches in Java and the Neighbouring Islands* (London, 1824).

——*Descriptive Catalogue of the Lepidopterous Insects in the Company's Museum*, 2 parts (London, 1828–29).

——*Plantae Javanicae Rariores* (London, 1838–52).

——*Catalogue of the Mammalia in the Museum of the Honourable East India Company* (London, 1851).

——*A Catalogue of the Lepidopterous Insects in the Museum of the Honourable East India Company*, 2 vols. (London, 1857 and 1858–59).

HORSFIELD, T. and MOORE, F. *A Catalogue of the Birds in the Museum of the Hon. East India Company*, 2 vols. (London, 1854–58).

    The Manuscripts of the two books above (*MSS. Eur. D. 171–2* and *B. 31–3*).

——Lists and Memoranda of Quadrupeds, Birds and Fishes from Java (*MSS. Eur. F. 52*).

MARSDEN, W. *History of Sumatra* (London, 1783).

——*A Brief Memoir of the Life and Writings of the late William Marsden, written by himself* (London, 1838).

McCLELLAND, J. 'Report on the Physical Condition of the Assam Tea Plant', *Transactions of the Agricultural and Horticultural Society of India*, IV, 1837, 1–58.

——'List of Mammalia and Birds collected in Assam', *Proceedings of the Zoological Society, London*, VII, 1837, 146–67.

——'On the fresh-water Fishes collected by William Griffith during his travels from 1835–42', *Journal of Natural History, Calcutta*, II, 1842, 560–89.

——*Sketch of the Medical Topography or Climate and Soils of Bengal and the North West Provinces* (London, 1859).

RAFFLES, T. S. *History of Java*, 2 vols. (London, 1817).

ROXBURGH, W. *Plants of the Coast of Coromandel*, 3 vols. (London, 1795–1819).

——*Flora Indica*, 2 vols. (Serampore, 1820–24).

ROYLE, J. F. *Illustrations of the Botany and other Branches of the Natural History of the Himalayan Mountains and of the Flora of Cashmere*, 2 vols. (London, 1839).

——'Account of the Botanic Garden at Saharanpur', *Journal of the Asiatic Society of Bengal*, I, 1832, 41–58.

——Report on the Botanical Collection in India House (Home Miscellaneous Series, 787).

SYKES, W. H. 'A Catalogue of the Mammalia observed in Dukhun, East India'. *Proceedings of the Zoological Society, London*. I, 1831, 99–105.

——'A Catalogue of the Birds observed in Dukhun, East Indies'. *Proceedings of the Zoological Society, London*. I, 1832, 77–99.

WALLICH, N. *Tentamen Florae Napalensis Illustratae*, 2 vols. (Calcutta and Serampore, 1824–26).

    Plantae Asiaticae Rariores, 3 vols. (London, 1830–32).

——A Numerical List of Dried Specimens of Plants in the East India Company's Museum, collected under the Superintendence of Dr Wallich of the Company's Botanic Gardens at Calcutta (*MSS. Eur. G. 32*).

CONCORDANCE OF VOLUME NUMBERS

Old Library shelf mark		Catalogue		Old Library shelf mark		Catalogue	
91 E	1	NHD	1	91 C	1	NHD 26	
	2		2		2	27	
	3		3		3	28	
	4		4		4	29	
	5		5		5	30	
	6		6		6	31	
	7		7		7	32	
	8		8		8	33	
	9		9		9	34	
					10	35	
89 C	1		10		11	36	
	2		11				
	3		12	MacKenzie, Book 22		37	
	4		13	23		38	
	5		14	Hardwicke. 91 E 19		39	
	6		15	Leyden. Oriental Album 74. 305.21 F		40	
	7		16	Blagrave		41	
	8		17	Chinese. Case 4.21		42	
	9		18	Case 4.26		43	
	10		19	Clive. Add. Or. 344–58		44/1–15	
	11		20	Howard		44/16, 17	
	12		21				
	13		22				
	14		23				
	15		24				
	16		25				

Drawings contained in the European manuscript collection and listed in the printed catalogue (Kaye, G. R. *Catalogue of Manuscripts in European Languages*, ii, part ii, section I, London, 1937) retain their manuscript numbers unchanged.

INDEX

Printed in England for Her Majesty's Stationery Office
by William Clowes and Sons, Limited, London and Beccles

Wt. P.10077. K. 8.   S.O. Code No. 88-5107★